REIGNING CATS & DOGS

Good Nutrition
Healthy Happy Animals

D0190355

Pat McKay

OSCAR PUBLICATIONS

REIGNING CATS & DOGS by Pat McKay

Front & Back Cover Artwork: Jeff T. Boley
Insert Coordinator: Kelly Deutsch

Oscar Publications, First edition, 1992
Oscar Publications, Revised edition, 1996
Oscar Publications, Third printing, August 1997
Oscar Publications, Fourth printing, April 1998
Oscar Publications, Fifth printing, October 1999
Oscar Publications, Second revised edition, May 2002

ISBN: 0-9632394-4-9

Library of Congress
Catalog Card Number: 92-93312

Printed in the United States of America on recycled paper.

This book is not intended, nor should it be regarded, as allopathic veterinary medical advice.

The fields of health and nutrition hold widely varying views. The intent of this book is to offer nutrition information to help you make an informed decision whether to use naturopathic methods of healing for your own animals, which is your constitutional right.

Oscar Publications
396 West Washington Boulevard
Pasadena, CA 91103
626-296-1120

TABLE OF CONTENTS

Brooks

Brooks, a gorgeous, sleek, black cat with a tiny cravat of white on his chest, was found by a mid-wife friend of mine in 1986. He wandered into her yard and her children, of course, wanted to keep one more kitten. They had five already, so mom said no. I took Brooks to my nutrition center in Los Angeles and let people know there was a black kitten available for adoption.

Well, as many of you who foster animals know, we fall in love with them while waiting for someone else to adopt.

Within a week or two some physical symptoms began to show up with Brooks. Lethargy, loss of appetite, runny stools, a temperature of 104 degrees. I started treating him with homeopathic remedies with little response. Very often, if you do not have the right remedy or the correct potency, there will be no reaction to it at all. I was now keeping Brooks with me twenty-four hours a day and taking his temperature several times a day because it was fluctuating from 103 to 108 degrees. He was a very sick cat. Keeping him hydrated was the most important part of keeping him alive at this point. Dehydration with any person or animal can happen fast and be fatal. Whenever there is a high temperature and/or diarrhea the most critical condition to pay attention to is dehydration.

The whole story is long and drawn out. This condition continued for approximately three months. During this time I consulted a homeopathic veterinarian who tried several remedies that were not effective. Then one day he called to suggest one that finally worked.

I have to preface the rest of the story by saying that with homeopathic remedies many times the symptoms get worse before they get better. The reason being that whatever toxins or disease the body is dealing with must come out of the system. It's like a sliver being in your finger; you have to cause more trauma by pulling it out, but until it is out, the body causes inflammation until the foreign object is removed.

Brooks' reaction was extreme; not typical by any means, but I want to tell you the story because it may help someone to go through a healing crisis that they feel is an ordeal. After you hear Brooks' story everything else is mild. However, I reiterate, this is not typical

Brooks cont.

and not meant to keep people from doing homeopathy, but to encourage the use of it, because of its miraculous healing properties.

A few hours after giving Brooks the remedy, we were in the den of my home when Brooks started coming at me with glaring eyes and a very cunning stalking, just as if to attack me. I tried to hold and comfort him, but he couldn't be still a second. He began to scratch and claw. I wrapped him in a towel to keep either of us from being hurt. He would not tolerate anything around him. He was getting more and more ferocious and aggressive and started throwing himself around the room. It was a scene right out of the Exorcist. I got a cat carrier and padded it with towels and confined him. The strength of his attack caused the carrier to be thrown around the room. I had to wedge it between the couch and the wall. The attack went on all night. Sometimes violent and sometimes just slight movement. But other than spraying him with Rescue Remedy, talking to him and playing soft music, I was not able to touch him or help in any way

When I would approach him, he would hunch up like a Halloween cat and hiss and carry on like he had never seen me before. I wondered what terrible hallucinations were going on in his mind.

For the next day or two he slept constantly which was certainly no surprise. His temperature broke; he started eating and acting like his own sweet self.

A couple of months later, he started with the same symptoms; I repeated the remedy; he went through a similar attack, although much, much less severe. Then again with even less severity he went through it again several months later for the last time.

Two years later we moved to Eugene, Oregon. He went to live on a goat farm and became the caretaker of baby chicks, ducklings and baby goats. For some reason he hunts only for show and tell; doesn't eat his catch; but eats his raw meat meals at the dinner table with his human companions, if you please.

A footnote about homeopathic remedies and their reactions. The above situation is the most dramatic I have ever experienced or even heard about. This is definitely not the typical response. I tell the story for its dramatic healing effect and because it is true and did happen. Brooks would have been a very sick and unhappy cat all his

Brooks cont.

life if this cure hadn't happened. Remember it's the body that cures itself. The body was given what it needed and used it to affect a cure.

Drugs would have just suppressed the problem. With drugs it appears at first they are working when the symptoms go away, but in fact, the drugs have only driven the disease deeper in the system to come out later as an even more severe condition, such as arthritis, cancer, heart problems, etc.

When I see people and/or animals who are chronically ill, I know there is at least one "foreign body" in the system – something that needs to come out or be put in balance. Suppressing such problems with drugs or cutting it out with surgery does not get to the cause. Natural remedies—when you can find the correct one—give the body what it needs to heal.

Most reactions to the correct homeopathic remedy are subtle and sometimes unnoticeable. In fact, if negative symptoms continue for more than forty-eight hours you can be quite sure you are taking or giving the wrong remedy or wrong potency. Constitutional homeopathic remedies are not to be taken without professional advice from a classical homeopath. Unfortunately there aren't too many practitioners for animals or for people, so you have to be diligent about looking for a good classical homeopath.

Sincerely,

Pat McKay
patmckay@gte.net

ANIMAL NUTRITION

Animal nutrition is easy, fun and rewarding. This book is devoted to giving you the necessary information on feeding your cats and dogs—the way Mother Nature intended—with fresh, wholesome foods.

With the following knowledge you will be able to provide a nutrition program for your animals which will solve many of their ailments, such as skin and coat disorders, allergies, arthritis, ear and eye problems, liver, kidney and bladder dysfunction, weight problems, constipation, diarrhea, indigestion, fleas, parasites, et al, that may have plagued your animal (and you) for months or years.

Ninety percent of the pathology (disease) in animals has to do with a poor diet. Once your dog or cat is receiving the proper nutrition, you will see all the difference in the world, even if you thought you already had a healthy animal.

With this information you will save your animal and yourself the stress and hassle of many medical problems.

Equally important, there will be less stress on your pocketbook as well.

CHAPTER 1

FRESH, RAW, WHOLE FOODS

The first question is "What do I feed my dogs and cats if I don't give them canned or dry food?"

Cats/Dogs Need Meat

Fifi and Tabatha may seem cute and cuddly on the outside, but on the inside they are identical to their sister wolves and lions in the wild. In 1993 the scientific community officially designated the dog and wolf as the same species (Canis lupus). The domesticated cat, Felis catus, is classified as belonging to the family of the flesh-eating, predaceous mammals, including the cougar, leopard, lynx, etc. Despite domesticating our companion cats' and dogs' behavior, they still have the identical organs, bone structure, biological and nutritional needs as that of a wolf or tiger – carnivores - meaning they need to eat fresh, raw meat to survive long, hearty lives.

Meal, bonemeal, meat by-products, dried animal digest, poultry by-products, liver glandular meal, dried liver digest, fish meal and fish by-products are typical ingredients of cat and dog food, all of which are highly cooked and processed and do not have the nutrients our companion animals need to have for optimum health.

Proper nutrition automatically boosts the body's natural resistance to disease.

The answer: Fresh, raw, whole foods.

Felines and canines in the wild eat mice, birds, reptiles and insects. If I were to suggest that you provide these various small wild animals to feed to your companion animals you would close the book at this point and say this author has flipped. It is not culturally accepted in our present society, any more than the eating of dogs and cats by people is accepted.

Our culture does, however, accept eating beef, lamb, chicken and turkey, so that is what we will discuss here, even though my preference is to feed what Mother Nature intended.

People who feel animals should eat cooked, processed and devitalized foods are the ones who profit from this practice. Commercial pet food manufacturers have convinced the consumer—to the tune of $9 billion a year—that canned and dry foods are the only way to go.

In the past fifty to sixty years we have been so inundated with processed foods, abusive drugs, needless surgeries, deadly pesticides, excessive vaccinations and quick fixes that we are going backwards fast.

We must take care of our animal's mind, body and spirit in healthy, natural ways. Artificial methods that put off simple problems, only to bring on more complicated ones later, do not serve our animals.

For instance, suppressing a flea allergy with cortisone, which later may cause the system to develop cancer, is no solution. Or feeding dry food—which causes kidney problems by virtue of not providing the digestive system with enough water—is not a convenience to you or your animal.

Vaccine Statistics

Researchers have linked an increase feline fibrosarcomas and other sarcomas at the vaccination site in cats. The study found a 61 percent increase in these lesions between 1987 and 1991, following the 1987enactment of a mandatory rabies vaccine law.

In humans, the death rate from measles in the mid-1970's (post vaccine) was exactly the same as it was in the early 1960's (pre vaccine). A 1993 British study shows the odds of suffering brain damage from the full series of DPT shots are one in 62,000. That is in addition to over 900 deaths per year caused by the vaccine. Since 1979 the only cases of polio in the U.S. have been caused by the oral polio vaccine, including 119 deaths from 1980 to 1994.

Please read: NATURAL IMMUNITY, Why You Should NOT Vaccinate by Pat McKay.

Today's animals are not doing well physically or emotionally. We are seeing more immune system problems, genetic disorders and chronic, deadly diseases than ever before.

The answer is to go back to the basics: fresh food, plenty of exercise and natural health care, providing enjoyment and quality of life.

The old adage—we are what we eat—is true. No matter what else we do for our companion animals, if we continue to feed them devitalized, processed foods out of cans and bags their health will continue to deteriorate. Each generation on commercial pet food has physical and mental problems that are more serious than the previous generation.

Within a few days on the fresh food program you will notice a spark in your animals' eyes that you have never seen before.

You will notice an overall healthy energy flowing throughout their bodies as the physical ailments begin to clear up.

You will see physical and emotional signs of health in your animals that you never dreamed possible.

This may take days or weeks, but it can't begin until you, the guardian—we are the guardians of our animals, definitely not their owners—start feeding fresh, raw, wholesome foods as Mother Nature intended.

CHAPTER 2

CARNIVORES ARE NOT VEGETARIANS

All dogs and cats must eat raw meat. If not, they are headed for serious trouble.

If they were living in the wild, they would be eating rodents, birds, reptiles, insects and other animal protein. The only vegetables and

---

Cats and Dogs are Carnivores

Cats and dogs are carnivores with teeth and claws designed to catch, rip and tear flesh. They have short small intestines designed to assimilate and eliminate food quickly so the meat of their prey does not putrefy in their systems. They have an acidic digestive system, enzymes and other biochemicals needed to digest the raw meat. Their internal workings, including their entire digestive system, and the way food is utilized for growth, maintenance, repair and reproduction is the same of their carnivore cousins in the wild.

Biologists have yet to discover any carnivore that eats only vegetation or that cooks its food prior to eating. Carnivores are designed to derive the nutrients they need from raw meat. Many successful zoos and other captive habitats have discovered that they cannot keep their animals healthy and able to reproduce unless they are fed raw food. Many performance trainers, like those who train police dogs, feed raw meat and vegetables, including raw bones.

Cats and dogs need lots of calcium. Feeding your cats and dogs without a calcium supplement will result in a calcium deficiency. Meat is significantly low in calcium so feeding meat and vegetables alone will cause a lack of calcium. Some signs of a calcium deficiency are arthritis; skin and coat problems; splayed feet; hip dysplasia; weak, easily injured ligaments and tendons; brittle or soft nails, tooth decay, broken bones; severe pain, bladder, liver and heart problems.

---

grains they would eat would be in the digestive system of their prey.

The definition of a carnivore is "any chiefly flesh-eating mammal, including dogs and cats."

I have heard all kinds of rationalizations for making dogs and cats vegetarians. Many vegans feel they are saving the life of a farm animal by feeding their companion animals just grains and vegetables.

First of all, it is not the dogs and cats of the world who are creating the destruction of this earth by the overabundant consumption of farm animals. It is the human beings. The people should be the vegetarians—not the carnivores. This world would be very well balanced if people ate vegetables and carnivores ate animal flesh.

The universe was perfectly designed by the wisdom of a greater spirit. We should not tinker with perfection.

Taurine

Carnivores must get their taurine from raw meat. It is an essential amino acid, especially for cats.

They cannot produce their own. High concentrations of taurine are found in chicken and beef hearts. The lack of this amino acid can cause epilepsy, edema, hyperactivity, hypoglycemia, blindness and death.

A few years ago the commercial pet food industry started adding taurine (some of which was a synthetic made from petroleum) to commercial pet foods. This is the equivalent of stripping bread of all its nutrients and then adding synthetic vitamins and calling it "enriched."

Avoid the taurine-deficiency problem altogether by simply feeding fresh, raw meats.

Fatty Acids

Most skin and coat problems are caused by a lack of fatty acids. The body cannot manufacture the essential fatty acid linoleic. Linolenic and arachidonic acids can be produced by the system only if linoleic is sufficiently supplied to the body from fresh raw foods.

Other disorders caused by a lack of fatty acids are high blood pressure, high cholesterol, arthritis, and diseases of the heart, brain, prostate gland and kidneys.

People need only 10 percent fat in their diets. Carnivores need at least 30 to 40 percent fat.

When buying meat for your animals 20 to 30 percent fat is required.

All fats must be eaten raw. Cooked fat is grease. Cats and dogs cannot assimilate grease.

It is vitally important that the meats be as chemically free as possible because the growth hormones, steroids and other drugs are stored in the fat of farm animals.

Raw meats provide the necessary saturated fatty acids.

Grape seed oil, flaxseed oil and hempseed oil which have the essential fatty acids, linoleic and linolenic, with naturally occurring vitamin E, provide a balance of unsaturated fatty acids, and should be refrigerated after opening.

Animals who would benefit from extra unsaturated fatty acids are ones with high cholesterol, skin and coat problems, and cats with hairballs. A daily dose of one-half teaspoon to two tablespoons, depending on the size of your animals, is recommended.

CHAPTER 3

MEATS AND OTHER PROTEINS

Proteins that are best for dogs and cats are beef, lamb, chicken, turkey, organ meats (liver, heart, kidney and gizzards), organic fish and egg yolks.

Other proteins, which are sometimes questionable because of pollutants or indigestibility are fish, dairy products, tofu and dry beans.

First let's talk about the ones that are the best. Animals raised organically and naturally range fed provide the very best quality of meats. Next would be the meats that are found in meat markets and supermarkets.

To find meats that are chemically free—no steroids or hormones—presents a challenge. Your health food store or independent meat market is the best source of information. They will either carry chemically free meats or tell you where you can find them. (If you are a meat eater, this same information is vitally important to your own health as well.)

Many of you are probably not even aware

that the farm animals in this country are fed and injected with growth hormones, steroids, antibiotics, vaccines and preservatives during their lifetime. All of these chemicals and drugs are supposed to make the farm animals grow unnaturally large, do so quickly, and make the meat more tender.

Our health pays a high price for this "tender" meat, because each one of these chemicals has side effects on both the farm animal and the one who eats the farm animal.

One example of serious carcinogenic side effects of a drug, diethylstibesterol (DES), was found to have caused cancer and other abnormalities in many of the children of women who took this prescribed drug during their pregnancies. The pharmaceutical and medical community continued to produce and prescribe this drug for over thirty years after proof that DES was a carcinogen.

During this same era, 1940 to 1979, DES was not only prescribed for pregnant women, but given to millions of farm animals to make them "juicier, meatier and faster growing." Anyone who ate meat during those forty years also received doses of DES. Some investigators believe that DES has a ten-to-twenty year lag time between exposure and development of cancer. Even though it was banned in 1979, people could be developing cancer from DES into the next century.

The reason for bringing this to your attention is that many people are not aware of how many debilitating drugs, hormones, steroids and other poisonous additives are given to farm animals while they are still alive. It isn't just the preservatives that are added to the meat after the animal is slaughtered, but the horrifying drugs and chemicals injected into them and fed to them during their lifetime.

DES is now off the legal market, but there is always the unconscionable farmer who continues to this day to illegally feed and implant his farm animals with DES.

Commercial growers are presently using different growth hormones and steroids that months or years from now may prove to be just as life threatening as DES. All of these drugs and chemicals are approved by the Food and Drug Administration (FDA) and the United States Department of Agriculture (USDA).

We must look out for ourselves, because

our own government condones these practices. DES is just one example of drugs in our food. I don't want to belabor the point. I do want to make it clear that it is not always easy to find good, naturally grown food in this country.

The more we keep insisting on range-fed animals and organically grown food, the better it will be for all of us. We can still reverse this trend of using chemicals. We the consumers have to make it known that we want naturally grown products.

Commercially Grown, Processed vs. Organic

Nature never designed the body to handle the volume of toxins found in commercially grown, processed food. This exposure to pesticides, herbicides, and other toxic chemicals can contribute to a variety of physical, psychological and neurological symptoms. Recent studies show increased cancer rates, arthritis, obesity, dental disease and heart disease in people chronically exposed to chemicals. Organically grown crops, however, have a lower content of carcinogenic nitrates, generally a higher vitamin C content, and better protein quality for easier, more efficient absorption when compared with crops grown with chemical fertilizers and pesticides.

Our companion animals are in equal danger with regard to toxins. One study revealed canned pet foods, no particular brand, with severe lead contamination. The lead levels ranged from 0.9 to 7.0 ppm in cat foods and 1.0 to 5.6 ppm in dog foods. What is alarming is daily intake of only six ounces of these contaminated foods could exceed the amount of lead considered toxic for children.

Muscle Meats and Organ Meats

Muscle meats (beef, lamb, chicken and turkey) are great sources of B-complex vitamins, phosphorus, iron, sulphur, copper and potassium. This animal protein is the staple of the diet and should be fed at least five days a week.

Organ meats (liver, kidney, gizzard and heart) are richer in vitamins and minerals and should be fed only once or twice a week.

Guardians tend to feed organ meats way too often. In fact, in some instances people have told me they feed liver every single day. This is much too rich and causes serious imbalances, especially with the oil soluble vitamins A, D and E.

Too much liver actually causes liver disorders, fat deposits that congeal and other physical problems.

Pork should not be fed to domestic animals because of the possibility of trichinosis, an organism which to be destroyed requires cooking. Because only raw meat can be properly assimilated by carnivores, pork would not be a good choice. It is also the most difficult meat to digest.

The order of easy digestibility of proteins is: eggs, chicken, fish, lamb, beef, turkey, dairy products and lastly pork.

Turkey and chicken, because they are both poultry, are often considered to be very similar. This is far from true. Turkey is a totally different meat. For one thing turkey is very high in L-tryptophan, an amino acid that acts as a tranquilizer.

Protein: Variety Is Key

Chicken and turkey may seem like similar proteins, as they are both poultry, however, on a nutritional level they are quite different. Each type of meat differs drastically in the nutritional details – not only in how amino acids makeup proteins, for example, but in the amount of vitamins, minerals and trace minerals that are found. So it is an absolute must to vary meats throughout the week to ensure that cats and dogs get the variety of nutrients they need.

Organ meats must be included in the general diet. They provide a rich source of nutrients not found in muscle meats. Organ meats are a rich source of B-complex vitamins, phosphorus, iron, sulfur, copper and potassium. Organ meats should be approximately 20 percent of the raw food program. If possible, add livers and kidneys of naturally raised animals to avoid toxicity from hormones and antibiotics found in commercially raised animals.

In the wild your carnivore cat or dog would ingest their entire prey: flesh, bones, blood, entrails (including organs), digested and undigested food in the stomach and intestines, hair, head, feet and tail. The only parts they do not utilize are teeth, nails, beaks and hoofs. To provide a comparable meal domestically is impossible, but we can come close to Mother Nature's design with a balance of raw muscle meat, organ meat, bones, fat and vegetables. Providing your dogs and cats raw chicken necks, chicken backs, chicken hearts, beef rib bones, marrow bones and knuckle bones, just to name a few treats, will add to their overall health.

Many times after eating holiday turkey, people feel they are extremely sleepy because they ate too much. Actually it is because of the L-tryptophan in the turkey.

This does not mean you should not feed turkey on a regular basis. It is an excellent protein. Just don't overfeed—you should be rotating all the proteins anyway.

Dogs and cats who are hyperactive would do well if fed turkey more often, especially in the evening when everyone would benefit from a good night's sleep.

Poultry and Salmonella

Because cats and dogs are carnivores and raw meat is their natural food, their digestive juices take care of salmonella, Escherichia coli and other unfriendly bacteria that often cause food poisoning in people. Many veterinarians oppose the feeding of raw meat and tend to unjustly blame salmonella, E coli and parasites when actually the problems come from a weakened digestive system and/or an autoimmune condition caused by feeding cooked foods. Enlightened veterinary practitioners realize this and encourage their clients to feed raw meat.

Natural Preservatives

In 18 years of working professionally with people and their animals, I have never heard of a case of salmonella or E coli from raw food. I have heard of salmonella from two different dogs eating **cooked** food, and the worst salmonella problem in the country in 1998 was several thousands pounds of **cooked** baby cereal that was contaminated and had to be recalled. So don't think because you are cooking the food you are necessarily killing the unfriendly bacteria.

Some people still feel so strongly about the situation that they want to do something. I do not recommend it, but you can use food-grade hydrogen peroxide, grapefruit seed extract or colloidal silver to prepare the meat before feeding. If I absolutely cannot convince you that it is not necessary, you may add one of the following: 1 tablespoon of 3 percent food-grade hydrogen peroxide OR 4 drops of grapefruit seed extract liquid concentrate OR 1 teaspoon of colloidal silver to 6 ounces of purified water and pour over one pound of ground poultry. Mix the liquid with the meat until it is completely absorbed into the ground meat.

Don't Bother Purifying

Now that I have given you the formula for purifying the poultry, let me remind you that cats and dogs great each other by sniffing and licking each others anuses; love to drink out of the toilet bowl; cats lick their feet after coming out of the litter box; dogs bury a bone, dig it up weeks/months later and relish every bite of the rotted meat and bone, maggots, insects, parasites, bad bacteria, viruses or fungi. Don't bother purifying.

Fish

Fish is an excellent source of protein, fatty acids, vitamins and minerals. But... are our fish healthy and edible anymore? Therein lies the question. First of all, there is a strong possibility that much of our fish is polluted with heavy metals, such as mercury and cadmium. Secondly, fish should not remain at room temperature for longer than an hour. Thirdly, you must be very knowledgeable about the condition, color and odor of fish to know that it is fresh and free of disease.

If you feel you have a good source of healthy fish, by all means, feed them to your animals.

Tilapia and some catfish are being organically farm raised and are safe to feed. Hopefully more and more fish will be healthy and fit to feed to our companion animals.

You need to be very careful that you do not feed fish bones, sharp fins and tails which can cause punctures and internal bleeding.

Fish

A report from Natural Resources Defense Council warns that over 52 million people a year who fish for recreation or subsistence are advised to limit or avoid fish consumption because of toxic contamination in a growing number of streams, rivers, lakes, and coastal areas.

These "fish advisories" rose more than 70 percent between 1993 and 1996 mostly due to improved analytical techniques. In 1996, the most recent year which nationwide data is available, there were 2,194 advisories in 47 states. Low or no advisories in a state is not an indication that state's waters are safer, however. States vary in their methods estimating the consumption risks of contaminated fish. For instance, FDA advisories balance the possible economic impacts of losses to the fishing industry with public health risks, while the EPA advisories are based on health risks alone making advisories questionable. Organically raised fish is generally safest.

Do not feed canned tuna. First of all it is cooked and most of the important nutrients for carnivores have been destroyed.

Secondly, animals, especially cats, become addicted very quickly to the taste, and then you cannot get them to eat anything else.

Again, as with liver, canned tuna causes an imbalance in the nutritional scheme of things, and in particular a deficiency of vitamin E.

Dairy Products

All dairy products, if they are fed at all, must be fed in their raw (unpasteurized) form, because once milk products are pasteurized they are very difficult to digest. The friendly bacteria necessary for digestion are destroyed during the sterilization process.

Animals in nature do not get any milk after they have finished nursing. And they never get cow's milk. Mother's milk of each species is totally different from one another. There is no resemblance between the mother's milk of canines, felines and bovines.

Another reason I feel dairy products should not be fed is because after four or five months of age the systems of dogs and cats do not produce enough lactase to digest the lactose in milk.

If you still choose to feed milk products, the easiest for your animals to assimilate would be cottage cheese, buttermilk, kefir, sour cream and yogurt because these dairy products have been curdled or soured.

White cheese with little or no salt and no food coloring is the only cheese suitable for digestion and should be fed only as an occasional treat.

Raw butter is an excellent source of vitamins A and D and fatty acids. It must be unpasteurized to retain these good qualities.

Yogurt contains B-complex vitamins and has a higher percentage of vitamins A and D than does the milk it was made from. Yogurt is a natural antibiotic and because it has a high content of acidophilus, a beneficial bacteria, it also aids in digestion. It goes without saying that I am talking about plain, natural yogurt, without sugar, flavorings or other additives.

Goat's milk yogurt is best for carnivores because it is higher in fatty acids than any other milk. Did you know that goat's milk comes out of the goat already homogenized? Dairies go to so much bother to homogenize cow's

---

Cow's Milk Vs. Human Milk

Humans are the only mammals that (a) drink milk after weaning and (b) drink the milk of other animals. However, nature intended each species to produce milk to be the ideal introductory food for the young of that particular species until the digestive tract of the young is fully developed. After the digestive tract is fully developed, there is no longer a need for the mother's milk so the body ceases to produce enzymes and its ability to digest milk because it is no longer needed.

Each species' milk, whether cat, dog, people or bovine, has a decidedly different makeup. Cow's milk is the ideal food for calves. It provides the nutrients they need to help them develop into very large, slow-moving, not-so-intelligent adults. Human infants have different nutritional needs. Human milk contains much more lactose than cow's milk. It is needed for the far greater brain development in humans over animals. Almost 100 per cent of the protein in human milk is digested by infants, whereas, only about 50 per cent of the protein in cow's milk is available to human infants.

---

milk, when, in fact, Mother Nature already provided us with naturally homogenized milk from goats. Isn't She smart?

Eggs

Eggs are an excellent source of complete protein and are easily digested. They contain all the essential amino acids and the following nutrients: vitamins A, B2, D and E, niacin, biotin, copper, iron, sulphur, phosphorus and unsaturated fatty acids. The egg yolk is the richest known source of choline, which is necessary for emulsifying or dispersing cholesterol throughout the system.

By the way, dogs and cats do not have the cholesterol problems that people have. Because they are carnivores, their systems assimilate fats and oils more efficiently. Raw fats and oils, of course.

If your animal is having a cholesterol problem, it is either because he or she is eating cooked meats or other processed proteins, or because the liver, which regulates cholesterol, is not currently functioning properly.

Egg yolks should be fed raw. The whites should be cooked until the clear part of the egg turns white. Egg whites can cause a loss of biotin in the system.

If you soft-boil an egg for one or two minutes that will kill any questionable enzymes.

Another suggestion is to put the whole egg (still in the shell) in hot water and let it soak for five minutes to destroy the avidin, which is the protein that interferes with the absorption of biotin.

Hard-boiled eggs should be fed very seldom, perhaps not at all, because cooking makes them very hard to digest.

Do not feed the shell under any circumstances. When animals eat eggs or eggshells in the wild, the shell is still very fresh and soft. After the egg is a few hours old or has been cooked, the shell hardens. The edges of the broken shell become very sharp, which can cause internal bleeding.

The main concern with eggs is their quality and freshness. Make sure they come from healthy, free-range-fed chickens that have not been fed antibiotics, hormones or other drugs.

Of course it goes without saying that chickens who are caged and mutilated by having their beaks and nails cut are so stressed that they cannot be healthy or produce quality eggs.

Organic eggs are much higher in nutritional value than regular commercial eggs. If the eggs are fertile as well, they will contain beneficial growth hormones.

Keep eggs in a covered container because they will stay fresh longer. Try to use the eggs within one week of purchase.

One to eight eggs at a meal, depending on the size of the animal, is about right. For small cats and tiny dogs, one egg per meal will be sufficient. For large cats and small dogs that weigh from 10 to 20 pounds, two eggs; dogs from 20 to 35 pounds, three eggs; 35 to 50 pounds, four eggs; 50 to 65 pounds, five eggs; 65 to 80 pounds, six eggs; 80 to 100 pounds, seven eggs; 100 pounds and over, eight eggs.

If you are traveling with your animal, eggs are one of the easiest fresh proteins to find. Eggs make a very economical meal at 10 to 15 cents apiece.

Soy Products

Tofu (soybean curd), tempeh (fermented soy curd) and miso (fermented soy paste) are all made from soybeans. Because these soy products have been curdled and/or fermented, they are easily digested.

Even though soy is very nutritious, it is a vegetable protein that contributes very different nutrients from animal protein. Soy products are to be fed occasionally and not as a regular substitute for animal protein.

CHAPTER 4

VEGETABLES

All vegetables are nutritionally wonderful. Some are better than others in certain unique ways. Some of them have characteristics that require caution when feeding.

Veggies (with very few exceptions) are to be fed raw. They must be put through a food processor until the pieces are about the size of

---

Vegetables And Food Bourne Disease

The Centers for Disease Control (CDC) has reported that the occurrence of food bourne disease increases during the summer months for all foods, including fresh produce. Following are some steps that you can take to reduce the risk of foodbourne illness from fresh produce: purchase produce that is not bruised or damaged. If buying fresh cut produce, be sure it is refrigerated or surrounded by ice. After purchase, put produce that needs refrigeration away as soon as possible. (Fresh whole produce such as bananas and potatoes do not need refrigeration.) Fresh produce should be refrigerated within two hours of peeling or cutting. Leftover cut produce should be discarded if left at room temperature for more than two hours. Wash hands often! Hands should be washed with hot soapy water before and after handling fresh produce, raw meat, poultry, or seafood. Wash surfaces often. Cutting boards, dishes, utensils, and counter tops should be washed with hot soapy water and sanitized after coming in contact with fresh produce, raw meat, poultry, or seafood. Sanitize after use with 3% Food Grade Hydrogen Peroxide. Don't cross-contaminate. Use clean cutting boards and utensils when handling fresh produce.

---

the head of a pin, because carnivores have very short, small intestines and they do not have the time during the digestive process to break down and assimilate large chunks of vegetables.

A food processor, blender or hand grater may be used depending on the quantity of vegetables you are preparing and their consistency.

The following information will provide helpful hints about vegetables and the importance of them to your animals.

Asparagus

Asparagus is in season for a very short time. When it is, take advantage because it is one of the most healthful foods.

Asparagus is high in carotene, selenium and vitamin C, yet low in sodium.

This tasty morsel is often loved by cats, so put it on your list of "bribe" foods.

When choosing asparagus the tips should be tight and purplish in color, not open or soft. If it has a strong odor it is too old. The thickness of the asparagus does not affect its flavor or the nutritional value.

Beans

Beans are very high in vegetable protein, fiber, potassium, iron and thiamine.

Fresh green beans (pod and all) should be fed raw and must be thoroughly broken down in a food processor because dogs and cats cannot digest the hull that surrounds the bean. Often the beans will go straight through the system and come out the other end looking like beans and/or they will cause a great deal of gastric distress.

Dry beans still retain all the above-mentioned nutrients even after being dried.

Cereal Grasses

Wheat and barley grasses have a high-nutrient content and are some of the highest in chlorophyll foods. They have 20% vegetable protein and contain trace amounts of B12, as well as many other nutrients. Wheat grass, in particular, can pick up more than ninety minerals out of the estimated possible 102 found in rich soil.

Also present in cereal grasses are the anti-oxidant enzymes superoxide dismutase (SOD) and special fraction P4D1. Both of these substances slow cellular deterioration and mutation and are therefore useful in the treatment of degenerative disease and the reversal of aging. P4D1 works by stimulating the renewal of RNA/DNA. It also has exceptional anti-inflammatory properties, even more powerful than those of steroids such as cortisone. SOD is the enzyme in healthy cells, which protects them from free radicals that form when toxins damage the body. SOD is either scarce or completely absent in cells that are cancerous.

Specific medicinal uses of wheat and barley grasses are the treatment of arthritis, bruises/wounds, burns, cancer and constipation.

They are an inexpensive source of good food. However, because of the flatulency (gas) problem caused by the enzyme inhibitors inherently in beans and the time required to prepare them properly, many of you may not want to feed beans to your animals.

Dry beans must be frozen, soaked, cooked and then mashed thoroughly before feeding. The freezing kills some of the enzyme inhibitors. Soaking and cooking kills others. The mashing breaks down the hull surrounding the bean.

For many of you this may be too much preparation time. So don't do it. Your animal will survive well without eating dry beans.

For those of you who don't mind the preparation time and may already be preparing them for yourself anyway, by all means feed beans.

Before cooking, store dried beans in your freezer. When preparing dried beans, start by covering them with boiling water and allow the beans to soak for four hours or more. Drain this water and start with fresh water to cook. If any beans float to the top, you should discard them.

To cook them, add water to the pot until it

reaches two to three inches above the beans. Cook until tender. Beans vary so much that the cooking time can be anywhere from one to three hours. Add extra water if necessary while cooking. Adding a few tasty herbs always livens the bean pot.

After they have cooled, put them in the blender or food processor to break down the hull. You may or may not have to add more water while processing, depending on how much water was absorbed during cooking.

Beets

Beets have a very deep cleansing effect. They can really purge the digestive and elimination systems, causing cramping and loose stools which may be uncomfortable. If your animal has a lot of toxins to get rid of, this purging action may be overwhelming.

Start very slowly with beets and do not repeat too often at first. Not more than once a week. Start with one teaspoon of ground beets for a cat or a small dog's meal, and up to two heaping tablespoons for a one-hundred-pound dog.

After feeding beets, the urine and feces may be red in color so don't be alarmed. I have received several calls from frantic people thinking their animal must have internal bleeding, when actually the red color was because of the beets. You may see the reddish color for up to three days after feeding beets.

Do not let my words of caution deter you from feeding beets. There is probably no better natural cleanser for the system.

Beets are high in copper, manganese and potassium.

Beets should be a very dark red color with fresh, crisp dark green leaves.

When putting the beets through the food processor include some of the greens as well.

Beets

Beets are a silicon-rich vegetable and a good source of folic acid that strengthens the heart, improves circulation, detoxifies and renews the blood by building red corpuscles and adding tone to the blood with minerals and natural sugars. Beets also benefit the liver and moisten the intestines and are considered to have significant tumor-inhibiting effects. Beets contain betaine, which stimulates the function of liver cells and protects the liver and bile ducts, as well as aids in constipation. Beets also treat nervousness and congestions of the vascular system.

Beet greens contain oxalic acid, which inhibits calcium metabolism; it is best to feed other beneficial greens such as romaine lettuce, kale, chard and dandelion greens when also serving beets.

Broccoli

Broccoli belongs to the cabbage family of anticancer vegetables.

Bones love broccoli because it is one of the best vegetable sources of calcium. The heart and blood love broccoli because of all the potassium, and the colon loves broccoli for the fiber. What's not to love?

Choose broccoli with small, closed, compact buds and firm stems. The color of the head should be a rich, dark green, free of yellowing. A purplish tint on the buds of some varieties is a sign of freshness.

To prepare, just put buds, stems and even leaves through the food processor. Discard stems only if they are dry or split.

Brussels Sprouts

Brussels sprouts, another cancer inhibitor, are extremely high in vitamin C, rich in protein, low in sodium, with moderate amounts of vitamin A, riboflavin, iron, potassium and fiber.

Look for sprouts that have firm tight heads that are heavy for their size. The core end should be clean and white. Avoid sprouts that are yellow or brown.

Cabbage

Cabbage soothes the stomach and intestines whenever there is a digestive problem.

Cabbage, when it is cooked, causes flatulency problems, but in its raw state is very helpful to the digestive system because of the high amounts of vitamins B5 and B6.

This anticancer vegetable is rich in vitamin C, low in calories and sodium, and is one of the few vegetables that contains vitamin E.

The best cabbages are heavy and solid with leaves that look crisp and colorful. It is one of the hardier fresh vegetables that will keep for two to three weeks in the refrigerator.

Raw organic sauerkraut deserves a mention because it too is helpful for digestion due to the additional beneficial bacteria from fermentation.

Carrots

Carrots, the staple of the vegetable world, are widely available all year-round, and fortunately, we are seeing more organically grown carrots all the time.

The sweet taste of carrots is enticing even to the most finicky of animals, so it is a good choice when first starting your dog or cat on the fresh food program.

Carrots are very high in beta carotene, which is the vegetable version of vitamin A. Tests have shown that dogs can convert carotene into vitamin A, but not much is known about how a cat's body uses carotene. We do know that it is imperative for cats to have vitamin A from an animal source which, of course, they get from raw meats.

Other pluses for carrots are the high fiber content, potassium and vitamin C.

Carrots

Carrots are nutritional supermen; they store a goldmine of important vitamins and minerals. They are rich in antioxidants beta carotene, alpha carotene, phytochemicals and glutathione, calcium and potassium, and vitamins A, B1, B2, C, and E, which are also considered antioxidants, protecting as well as nourishing the skin. They contain a form of calcium easily absorbed by the body. Finally they contain copper, iron, magnesium, manganese, phosphorous and sulphur. These antioxidants fight free radicals and help prevent them from causing membrane damage, DNA mutation, and lipid (fat) oxidation, all of which may lead to many of the diseases that we consider degenerative. Carrots benefit the lungs; strengthen the spleen-pancreas; improve liver functions; aid in constipation; dissolve accumulations such as stones and tumors; treat indigestion; used for diarrhea and chronic dysentery and contain an essential oil that destroys pinworms and roundworms.

Carrots should have a bright orange-red color, and if they still have their tops, they should be bright green in color, fresh and crisp looking.

If you can get organic carrots, it is not necessary to peel or scrape the skin. By all means include a bit of the green carrot tops when processing the carrots, but using all of the tops would be way too many carrot greens.

When storing carrots it is best to snap off the tops so they do not draw the water from the carrots. Keep in a tightly closed plastic bag in the refrigerator.

As a matter of fact, each different vegetable should be kept in a separate plastic bag or container because some cause others to be bitter.

Cauliflower

Cauliflower, low in sodium, high in fiber, vitamin C, potassium and zinc, is another of the cancer preventing vegetables.

A good head of cauliflower should be firm and compact, white to ivory in color, surrounded by leaves that look tender and green. Brown spots on the head indicate that it's past its peak of freshness.

Purple cauliflower and broccoflower are now becoming popular. They offer the same great nutrients, so if the price is right, they are fine as well.

Celery

Celery, along with parsley, is a natural diuretic that helps with arthritis, urinary problems, water retention and chemical imbalances.

Celery is a high-energy food with lots of chlorophyll. Even the high sodium content is in a healthy natural form. Because dogs and cats love the salty flavor, I often add celery to my vegetable mixture.

Choose stalks that are a deep green and have not been blanched. Avoid yellow leaves or cracked stalks.

Corn

Corn, with its sweet taste, low sodium, moderate iron, zinc and potassium, is a good source of vegetable protein.

Even though the kernels are small they still must be put through the food processor to break down the hull surrounding each kernel of corn. Most carnivores cannot digest corn in its whole form.

NEVER give your dog or cat a corncob to chew on. If they should bite off a chunk of the cob and swallow it, it may lodge somewhere in the esophagus or the intestines causing a blockage which may require surgery.

When selecting corn be sure the husks are green and the corn silk is a fresh yellow-green around the cob itself. When opening the husks make sure the kernels are plump and full.

Corn silk is wonderful for urinary disorders. Make a tea from the fresh corn silk and see if your dog or cat will drink a little of it and/or pour it in their food. Good for the ol' kidneys.

Greens

My favorite greens are kale for its high vitamin content, dandelion for its blood building and purifying abilities and Swiss chard for its calcium and folic acid.

Many greens have a sharp taste and are not necessarily a favorite with carnivores. Dandelion, kale and Swiss chard are mild enough that they seem to blend in well with other sweeter vegetables.

Parsley, one of the best diuretics, should be fed in small amounts.

All greens are high in vitamins A and C, fiber and many minerals. Whatever ones your animals like will be good for them.

Look for bright, lively green color with tender leaves. Avoid greens that look limp or yellowed. The larger the leaves the greater chance it will be bitter.

All greens must be put through a food processor or blender.

Kohlrabi

Kohlrabi is a German word meaning cabbage turnip. That describes it beautifully. It has a cabbage taste and looks like a turnip. The greens and the bulb can both be eaten.

When it comes to vitamin C and potassium kohlrabi takes the lead.

To select kohlrabi choose the smaller, more tender globes with crisp leaves and stems. If you get tender kohlrabi it doesn't have to be peeled before being put in the food processor.

Lentils

Lentils are in the legume family of plants, which includes peas, beans, lentils and peanuts.

All legumes are high in vegetable protein, iron, thiamine, riboflavin and niacin.

Lentils take much less time to prepare than beans; however, they do have to be cooked thoroughly and put through the food processor because lentils have a hull just like beans.

Lentils look like tiny disks and come in a variety of colors including red, orange, green, tan and gray.

When sprouted they are rich in vitamin C.

Okra

Okra is also known as gumbo and lady's fingers. It has a short season from late summer to early fall.

Okra is a high-energy food with plenty of carotene, vitamins B-complex and C.

The smaller the okra the more tender it is. However, if you are putting it in the food processor the larger ones are okay. They will just contain more fiber.

Parsnips

Rich in insoluble fiber, parsnips are very good for the colon occasionally, but not as a steady diet.

Choose parsnips that are small in size, smooth, firm and creamy white in color.

They do not have to be peeled before putting them through the food processor.

Peas

Peas are high in magnesium and soluble fiber. If you use snow peas or sugar snaps you can put the whole vegetable, peas and pod, through the food processor. Their sweet taste makes them a favorite.

When choosing peas make sure they are plump, firm and a bright green, without gray blotches.

Dried peas, before feeding to carnivores, must be treated with the same thoroughness as other lentils.

Pumpkin

Pumpkins have such a wonderful, sweet flavor. You won't have any trouble getting your animals to eat them.

In addition to their very high fiber content, pumpkins boast good amounts of vitamin A, most of the B's, calcium, copper, magnesium, potassium and zinc. What a deal.

Pumpkins come in many sizes, shapes and varieties. Unless the skin is very hard, it is not even necessary to peel them before putting them through the food processor.

Baking and steaming is okay too, because even after cooking, they retain most of their nutritional value.

Alfalfa Sprouts

Alfalfa is considered more nutritionally concentrated than other sprouts. Primarily because the tiny alfalfa seed produces a root that can reach 100 feet into the earth, where it has access to minerals and trace elements untouched by other plants. Alfalfa's most important nutrients include rich plant protein, carotene, calcium, iron, magnesium, potassium, phosphorus, sodium, sulfur, silicon, chlorine, cobalt and zinc. Alfalfa also contains vitamins K and P (bioflavonoids) and abundant chlorophyll.

Alfalfa, radish, broccoli, clover and soybean sprouts contain concentrated amounts of phytochemicals (plant compounds) that can protect against disease. Canavanine, an amino acid analog present in alfalfa, demonstrates resistance to pancreatic, colon and leukemia cancers. Plant estrogens in these sprouts function similarly to human estrogen but without the side effects. They increase bone formation and density and prevent bone breakdown. Radish sprouts have 29 times more vitamin C than milk and 4 times the vitamin A found in milk.

Sprouts

Sprouts, the beginning of life for plants, offer many special nutrients to animals when eaten during this sprouting period. The most popular are alfalfa sprouts and bean sprouts, however all the others are just as nutritious and delicious.

When choosing sprouts make sure they are fresh and moist. Once they reach their peak of freshness, they lose their food value quickly.

Squash

Zucchini is my favorite because of its internal cleansing properties, its mild flavor and its nearly year-round availability. Other summer squash such as yellow crookneck and pattypan (scallop squash) have similar nutritional qualities, so take advantage of them during the summer months.

Winter squash, acorn, butternut and hubbard, are actually higher in most nutrients, but because of their hard rind bake or steam them rather than trying to peel the skin. Because I don't like to cook, I find that I don't feed winter squash as often as summer squash.

One of the pluses of winter squash is its long storage life.

All winter squash should have a hard rind, feel heavy and have stems.

Summer squash should have a bright, shiny skin, feel firm and have their stems still intact.

Summer squash can be put through the food processor, stem and all.

If you feed winter squash raw you must peel off the hard rind first before putting it in the food processor.

Sweet Potatoes

Sweet potatoes are extremely high in vitamin A. There have been considerable studies on their potential to reduce the risk of lung cancer in people. If your animal is exposed to cigar or cigarette smoke or exhaust fumes I would suggest feeding sweet potatoes often.

Sweet potatoes and yams are constantly being confused and the names are often used interchangeably. Whatever you call them doesn't change their great nutritional value.

Choose sweet potatoes that are firm and nicely shaped with a bright color. The colors can vary from tan, toast, brownish red to burgundy red.

Do not peel before putting through the food processor.

Turnips and Rutabagas

Both of these vegetables have come to the rescue during the winter months when other fresh vegetables were hard to find. Their taste is a bit snappy, but after your animals have been on the fresh food program awhile, they will enjoy something slightly different.

Even though they are a little on the starchy side, they are both chock-full of nutrients.

Turnips should be small, round, firm and creamy white to violet. If they come with the greens, all the better.

Rutabagas vary in color from creamy white to soft orange. They should be crisp and firm, not spongy or wrinkled.

Tender, fresh turnips and rutabagas need not be peeled before running through the food processor.

Nightshade Vegetables

Potatoes, tomatoes, peppers and eggplant are of the nightshade family. They have great nutritional qualities each in their own way. However, if your animal is having any symptoms of arthritis, inflammation, parasites, worms, respiratory problems or any other conditions that involve swelling or mucous, stay away from the nightshade family.

If your animal is healthy, with none of the mentioned problems, feel free to feed these vegetables occasionally. They should all be cooked before feeding.

Lettuce, Radishes & Others

Lettuce, radishes, cucumbers, spinach, onions and garlic all have a little something that causes concern.

Lettuce has little food value compared to other greens. Because everything animals eat needs to be as full of nutrients as possible, I suggest feeding kale, chard, endive or other greens instead of lettuce.

Many people give leftover salad to their animals. Most dinner salads contain iceberg lettuce (which is grown for shipping, not eating), raw tomatoes, green peppers, cucumbers and onions, all of which are extremely difficult for carnivores to digest.

Occasionally I make up a potato and onion soup to serve to my animals. That's the only time I use onions.

Raw garlic can be fed in small amounts, however, I prefer aged garlic for therapeutic use.

Spinach is high in oxalates (oxalic acid) which reduces iron absorption. It's fine to feed raw or steamed spinach once in awhile but, not as a steady diet.

Genetically Engineered Foods

Genetic engineering (GE) is a process by which genetic material inside the cells of living organisms are blocked, added, or scrambled to achieve desired traits. Biotechnologists say GE crops produce higher yields, create their own pesticides and are more nourishing, but critics suggest GE crops have the potential to cause vast damage. Cornell University scientists have shown pollen from GE crops can harm insects. Researchers have identified herbicide-resistant genes "migrating" into nearby weeds making the weeds stronger. Other scientists are concerned antibiotic-resistant genes will transfer to bacteria in people's organs, which could lead to the growth of an antibiotic-resistant disease strain or the potential for new toxins and allergens to become present.

The secret to a well-balanced diet is to use a variety of vegetables at each meal.

There are so many wonderful vegetables to choose from, do not get hooked—or let your animals get hooked—on the same ones day after day.

Whenever possible use organic vegetables. Many health food stores and even some supermarkets have them available now.

Most cities and towns have fresh produce markets on certain days of the week at parks and recreation areas where people who raise their own vegetables come to sell their produce. Ask them how they raise their products and if they are chemically free.

Organic vegetables do not have to be peeled or scraped. Just wash them lightly so the dirt and sand do not get into the food processor.

If you are not able to get organically grown produce, then soak the vegetables for 10 to 15 minutes in purified water with a tablespoon of raw (unpasteurized) apple cider vinegar or a few drops of grapefruit seed extract.

Frozen vegetables can be fed if necessary. They are handy to keep on hand for emergencies. Most frozen vegetables are blanched before freezing so they will have lost some of their nutrients. But considering there are no vegetables in commercial pet foods, frozen veggies are way up there on the nutritional ladder.

Put frozen vegetables through the food processor just like the fresh ones.

Canned vegetables should not be used because of the high salt and sugar content, plus they have been cooked.

Of course, the ultimate is having a garden and raising your own vegetables.

Sprouting: The Unlocking Of Nutrients

The process of germination or sprouting changes grains into living foods rich in vitamins, trace minerals, the carbohydrate-digesting enzyme amylase, amino acids, and other nutrients. Research shows as much as 25 times more vitamin K and 12 times more carotene in grain after it has sprouted. B-complex vitamins such as pantothenic acid typically increase up to 200 percent, vitamin B12 over 500 percent, pyridoxine 600 percent, and riboflavin nearly 150 percent. Grains fed sprouted to your cat or dog is acceptable – but only if they are fed in this manner.

Use organically raised wheat, rye, spelt, kamut, barley, oats, millet, buckwheat, or other sprouted grains from a health food store, macrobiotic supply company or sprout catalog. Rice is the only grain for which this process is not recommended.

Soak _ to 1 cup grain in a wide-mouth quart jar of water to which you have added 10 drops of liquid grapefruit seed extract, an all purpose disinfectant or 1 tablespoon of 3% food-grade hydrogen peroxide. Soak the grain 10 to 12 hours or overnight. For increased mineral content, add a pinch of powdered or liquid kelp to the soak water.

Health food stores sell plastic sprouting lids for wide-mouth quart jars or you can create a sprouting lid with cheesecloth and a rubber band. With the sprouting lid in place, drain the jar well, and then lay it on its side in a warm place away from direct sunlight. Ideal sprouting temperatures are between 70 and 80 degrees Fahrenheit.

After 24 to 36 hours, you will see small white roots emerge from the grain. If you don't see this growth on almost every seed by the second day, your grain is not viable and should be discarded. Assuming that it's sprouting, let it grow another day, then puree the grain in a blender or raw food processor.

Add a tablespoon of raw unheated honey (a source of carbohydrate-digesting amylase) and/or _ teaspoon of an enzyme powder containing amylase and let the mash stand at room temperature for an hour or two before refrigerating. This gives the amylase a chance to work, further breaking down and predigesting the grain acceptable for cats and dogs.

To introduce predigested/sprouted (uncooked) grain to your dog or cat, start with 1 teaspoon per 10 pounds of body weight every other day and gradually increase that amount as desired. Again, these grains must be sprouted and mashed using the process above for your carnivore to properly digest them or you may see serious digestive problems.

CHAPTER 5

GRAINS

Or, better yet, no grains at all! I now believe as well as many holistic veterinarians that grains are not necessary for carnivores, because the nutrients found in grains are readily available from the meat, bones and vegetables and supplements already provided in the raw food program.

In the wild, grains are not a significant part of the natural diet of canines and felines, even for mice or other prey animals.

One of the main reasons grains are added is because they are inexpensive, and secondly, we have become so used to the idea that they should be part of the diet.

For the past several years my own dogs and cats have been eating their fresh raw food meals without grains, and I see a decided improvement in their overall health, especially, digestion and stools.

The interesting part is that they are eating considerably less in volume which more than makes up for the higher cost of meat and vegetables as compared to grain.

The reason I continued to search for another formula is because my cocker-mix has a chronic yeast infection (Candida albicans) which is exacerbated by grains containing gluten.

The problem improved 50 percent in the first few months and continues to improve by discontinuing the grains. Even rice, millet and legumes which are ordinarily acceptable did not work for her.

Symptoms of Candida albicans are excessive scratching, licking, chronic eye and/or ear infections, rashes, hot spots, colitis, chronic cough, vaginitis, kidney and bladder infections, arthritis, hypothyroidism and even diabetes.

Celiac disease is another intestinal disorder (although more rare) that is caused by the intolerance of some animals to gluten, a protein that is in barley, oats, rye and wheat. Malnutrition often accompanies this disorder because of the greatly reduced absorption of nutrients.

Symptoms of celiac disease include nausea, diarrhea, abdominal swelling, foul-smelling stools, weight loss, anemia and skin rashes.

Dogs and cats can certainly have an occasional treat, like a cookie or biscuit, that is made from grains, or a rice cake. The dessert chapter has a quick recipe for cookies and other fun puddings you can share with your animals.

In the past year I have seen so many animals improve overall just by coming off the grains that I feel grains should not be fed on a regular basis. Because of this I am excluding the information about grains that was in the first edition of my book.

If you have been feeding your animals the raw food program with grains, please feed them just meat, vegetables, bones, calcium and the other supplements for one month and see what a difference it makes.

The importance of raw meat and vegetables in a canine or feline diet is seldom an issue in the traditional world of veterinary care. Certainly no advice is given about what raw whole foods your animals should be eating for specific health disorders.

One of the "food tips" you do hear suggested by medical practitioners is cooked hamburger and white rice for diarrhea.

I can't think of anything worse. Oh, it may stop the diarrhea, but so will a cork.

It definitely doesn't get to the cause of the diarrhea, nor does it make it easy on the stomach and the colon. The thought of stuffing the system with grease and starch to clog the plumbing boggles the mind.

The problems of constipation and diarrhea are solved with wholesome, raw meat and vegetables which provide the necessary nutrients and fiber.

CHAPTER 6

FRUITS

Some dogs and cats love fruit. For those that do, here are a few important guidelines.

1) Only one family of fruits should be fed at a time.

Irradiated Food

Irradiation is a means by which meat, poultry, fish and vegetables are treated with ionizing radiation from high-energy electron beams, X-rays, Cobalt 60 or Cesium 137 to kill pathogens and preserve shelf life. Although ionizing radiation reduces a number of potentially harmful bacteria and parasites, it does not eradicate all pathogens.

Irradiation turns fat into carcinogenic aflatoxins, which may produce cancer-causing cells, plus it destroys molecules in the food and creates free radicals. The free radicals bounce around in the food destroying up to 80 percent of vitamins A, C, E, K and B complex. Plus, these free radicals wipe out the natural digestive enzymes found in food. This means the body has to work hard to create its own enzymes to try to digest the food. The free radicals also combine with existing chemicals (like pesticides) in the food to form new chemicals, called Unique Radiolytic Products (URPs). Some of these URPs are known toxins. Long-term effects of these new chemicals in our diet have not been tested. The longest human study was 15 weeks.

---

2) Fruits should be fed on an empty stomach because they go through the digestive system very quickly, in approximately 20 to 30 minutes.

3) Let at least 30 minutes elapse before feeding anything else so that the fruits do not mix with the other foods and cause fermentation.

4) Blueberries and other small fruits with skins might not be able to be digested and may go through the system without breaking down. Be sure to check your animals' stools to make certain they are able to assimilate these fresh fruits.

Apples

Apples are an excellent source of pectin which is one of the seven forms of fiber. Pectin removes toxins, reduces the risk of heart disease and, because it slows the absorption of sugars, is beneficial for diabetic animals.

Apples are the one fruit that can be mixed with vegetables.The sweetness of apples enhances the food for those who like a sweet taste.

Apples are available all year-round. Their peak season is September through March.

Bananas

Bananas are a favorite because of their high natural sugar content. They are rich in minerals, especially potassium and magnesium.

Underripe bananas are difficult to digest, but fully ripened ones are soothing to the intestines and useful for treatment of diarrhea and colitis.

When the banana skin is yellow and speckled with brown, it is ripe and ready to eat.

It is okay to refrigerate them after they are ripe. Even though the skin turns dark brown that will not affect the flesh or the flavor.

Berries

Berries, rich in vitamins A and C, potassium and fiber, are fun to eat. However, remember, carnivores don't break down the skin surrounding each berry easily. Each animal is very much an individual in this regard. Check your animal's stool and see what's happening.

When I lived in Oregon, blackberries grew wild on our land. Often I would see Sally, my Doberman, pull blackberries off the bushes. She was very selective, picking only the plumpest, sweetest and juiciest of berries.

Citrus Fruit

Not many dogs and cats are interested in oranges, tangerines, grapefruit, lemons and limes. However, if they are, these fruits are a rich source of vitamin C.

The white membrane just under the peel contains bioflavonoids which are needed by the body to absorb vitamin C.

If you are eating citrus fruit, remove the membrane from the skin and share at least that part with your companion animal. Do not feed the peel of the citrus fruit because it is poisonous. Lemon juice has been used externally for fleas, however, I do not recommend that anymore.

Melons

Melons are a special class of fruits all by themselves, and they should be fed separately from other fruit families. Because they are practically all water, they go through the system very quickly and are excellent organ cleansers, especially for the kidneys. Melons are a great source of vitamins A and C and potassium.

During hot summer days, a breakfast of any of the melons is refreshing and nourishing.

Peaches

Peaches, apricots and nectarines are high in vitamins A and C and, unlike most fruits, contain calcium. Be sure to remove the pit or stone of these fruits before feeding to your animal.

Raisins & Grapes

A relatively recent revelation from Animal Poison Control Centers is that raisins and grapes are both considered toxic to dogs now. Kidney failure is the common result. This study is in its early stages. Why, how many and if it's specific to some breeds hasn't been answered yet.

Avocados

Avocados, a fruit, which are commonly considered a vegetable, are a good source of protein, vitamin E and contain up to 22 percent fat, most of which is monosaturated. They are excellent for animals having skin problems or who are underweight.

They are also a fruit that can be added directly to your animals' food, just like apples.

Any other fruits that you enjoy can certainly be given to your animals. Share a little with them . . . unless your animal has a yeast infection. Then, absolutely no fruit.

CHAPTER 7

PURIFIED WATER

If you live in an area where you feel the water is safe, that's great. Otherwise providing yourself and your animals with purified water is essential.

Water is not only the most abundant nutrient found in the body (approximately two-thirds of a dog's or cat's body weight), it is also by far the most important nutrient.

Water is responsible for and involved in nearly every body process, including digestion, absorption, circulation and excretion. It is the primary transporter of nutrients throughout the body and is necessary for all building functions. Water helps maintain a normal body temperature and is essential for carrying waste material out of the body.

Studies indicate many of our city water supplies are liberally laced with asbestos, pesticides, heavy metals like lead and cadmium, arsenic, nitrates, sodium and a variety of chemicals that are known carcinogens.

Is it any wonder our animals have arthritis, upper respiratory diseases, allergies, cancer, heart, liver and kidney disorders, urinary infections, poor teeth and gums, ear and eye infections and chronic skin problems?

It is imperative that your animals (and you) drink only pure water.

Boiling tap water only makes it worse because the purest water will be lost in the form of steam and any heavy metals or nitrates will be even more concentrated.

Even rainwater these days collects atmospheric pollutants as it descends.

If you continue to give tap water, the contaminants in the water can defeat your other nutritional efforts.

Purified water has a high degree of oxygen which not only makes it healthier but makes it taste better as well.

All drinking water and water used to prepare their food should be pure.

If you are not sure about the condition of your water have it tested. Most water purification companies will come to your house and test your water free of charge.

Do not get your purified water from vending machines. Bacteria builds up on the filters and the water is again contaminated. Otherwise they use chlorine to control the bacteria and you are back to chemically treated water. A reverse osmosis unit in your home is presently the most effective and inexpensive way to provide purified water.

Or you can buy bottled water in a food store or have it delivered, depending on the amount of water you consume.

It is true that most of the minerals are depleted from purified or distilled water. However, minerals will be in the fresh food and, if necessary, liquid minerals can be added to the food and the drinking water as a nutritional supplement.

Pure water added to your animal's food is vitally important to carnivores, especially cats, because this is the most efficient way for their bodies to assimilate water.

Cats are basically savanna animals and ordinarily will not drink water more than once or twice a week at most.

If your cats are drinking water on a daily basis they have a problem. However, you will notice after they have been on the fresh food program for a short time that they will practically stop drinking water from their water bowl and this is as it should be.

WATER, WATER EVERYWHERE...

Many drinking waters are available now, some of them flavored or carbonated, so be sure to look on the label. If there is any flavoring or sugars in any form, do not use them for your cats and dogs. There are some healthy sports waters available that are formulated from distilled water which have been further purified and filtered, sodium free, and contain none of the undesirable impurities often present in well or spring water. Some of these waters have been fortified with electrolytes and supplemented with potassium, magnesium, calcium, manganese and chromium to provide vital elements that are often lost through poor nutrition, illness and stress.

Water Catalysts

Water catalysts that reduce the surface tension of water by means of electrically charged ions can be very effective to help you and your animals utilize the purified water more efficiently. These water catalysts are especially beneficial for kidney, liver and heart ailments. Check our website for current products and the availability.

CHAPTER 8

NUTRITIONAL SUPPLEMENTS

Balanced nutritional supplements, including vitamins, minerals and herbs are vitally important to your animals' health.

Nutritional Supplements

Are the supplements you buy at the heath food store authentic food vitamins? Or are they chemically reacted synthetic vitamins? Well, let us just say most all vitamins sold, even in health food stores, are made up of more than 90% synthetic material.

Authentic vitamins, which are vitamins that exist within plants and living organisms, are organized into extremely subtle, complex patterns and are coupled with many other nutrients. These patterns cannot be duplicated in a laboratory simply because scientists are only aware of some, not all of Mother Nature's subtle complexities. So the compounds of which authentic vitamins are made are absolutely absent in all synthetic vitamins. Only supplements literally grown in a culture can maintain the bioavailability and complexity Mother Nature created. Pat McKay, Inc. is the only company providing these living, plant-cell grown supplements for animals. These are authentic vitamins and minerals with non-denatured vegetable protein, complex carbohydrates, bioflavonoids, bioflavonols, lipids and countless other food constitutes with their natural food attachments and enzymes, and they are consistent with what food represents to the body ensuring up to 95% absorbability.

BALANCE is the key word. Only your animal's body knows what vitamins or minerals are needed at any given time. As guardians all we can do is to provide nutritional supplements to make sure that all bases are covered. What the body doesn't need at the moment will be stored or eliminated depending on the type of supplement and the body's need.

Do not give one specific vitamin or mineral on an on-going daily basis for long periods of time.

For example, just because you read an article or a friend suggests giving a certain vitamin or mineral for your dog's skin problem, don't arbitrarily start giving it.

First of all, it may not be the lack of that particular nutrient that is causing the problem.

Second, by giving daily doses of any one vitamin/mineral, the body now has to come up with other supportive nutrients necessary to assimilate that one particular supplement. And when it cannot—because you are not supplying them—it can cause other imbalances within the nutritional scheme of things.

Third, the deficiency of any one vitamin or mineral may be caused by the body not having the essential nutrients like digestive enzymes to absorb it, so no matter how much of that one vitamin or mineral you give, the body is not able to assimilate it.

Fourth, your animal may be taking in excessive pollutants which interferes with the absorption of vitamins and minerals in general.

Fifth, you may be causing other problems, such as high blood pressure, inflammation or whatever, which can happen when you give one particular nutrient repeatedly.

This does not mean vitamins and minerals are not wonderful and necessary supplements. However, giving any supplement without balancing it in the diet not only causes an imbalance, but can have serious side effects.

My whole point is—always give a well-formulated balance of vitamins and minerals on a regular basis, and for special ailments, give the one particular vitamin or mineral just for the time it is needed, not forever.

The following general information on the function of vitamins is to give you an overall introduction into what they are, why they are so important, the problems that can be caused by the deficiency, and how they all work together as a family.

The two main families of vitamins are oil soluble vitamins A, D, E and F, and water soluble vitamins B, C and P. Oil soluble vitamins can be stored in different areas of the body and used as needed, provided your animals' organs and glands are healthy. Water soluble vitamins go out in the urine within three to four hours after ingesting them and must therefore be given more often.

Vitamin A

Just to mention a few important functions of vitamin A: maintains smooth, soft, disease-free skin and other body tissue; necessary for proper digestion of proteins; builds strong bones, teeth, eyes and blood; reduces infection

Deficiency of vitamin A can cause allergies, loss of appetite, skin and coat disorders, arthritis, cystitis, diabetes, soft teeth, upper respiratory congestion and infections.

Factors interfering with the absorption of vitamin A: mineral oil, sugar, cortisone, liver disorders and stress.

Vitamin D

Vitamin D, the sunshine vitamin, plays a great role in the family of oil soluble vitamins: regulates the thyroid; maintains the nervous system, heart action and blood clotting;

necessary for the proper balance of calcium and phosphorous; improves skin respiration.

Deficiency of vitamin D can cause poorly developed teeth, bones and muscles, kidney disorders, allergies, poor metabolism, arthritis, cystitis, diarrhea and irritability.

Factors interfering with the absorption of vitamin D: not enough exposure to sunlight and insufficient calcium and phosphorous.

Vitamin E

Vitamin E's primary function is to maintain the correct balance between oils, fats and amino acids in the body.

Other functions are: antioxidant; improves skin, muscles and nerves; slows the aging process; increases blood flow and urine excretion.

Deficiency of vitamin E can cause adrenal gland, pancreas, kidney, heart and liver disorders; abnormal fatty deposits and loss of collagen.

Factors interfering with vitamin E are iron, chlorine and taking of synthetic hormones.

Vitamin F

Vitamin F is a fat soluble vitamin consisting of unsaturated fatty acids (UFA). Vitamin F balances the saturated (animal fats) and the unsaturated (vegetable oils) fatty acids. Oleic, linoleic, linolenic and arachidonic acids are all part of the UFA FAMILY.

Important functions of vitamin F (UFA): lubrication of all cells; essential to vital organs and glands, especially the thyroid and adrenal glands; nourishes skin cells, mucous membranes and nerves; essential for all skin and coat disorders.

Deficiency of vitamin F can cause heart problems, diarrhea, cystitis, loss of hair, dermatitis and other skin and coat problems.

Because fleas thrive on malnourished skin, fatty acids are critical for natural flea control.

Factors interfering with the absorption of vitamin F: cooking of fats and oils, lack of bile, steroids, X-rays and other radiation.

The best sources of oil soluble vitamins A, D, E and F are found in raw meats, raw vegetables, cold processed vegetable oils and fish oils.

Water Soluble Vitamins

The water soluble vitamins B, C and P are as essential as the oil soluble vitamins. Maybe even more so, because the body cannot store these vitamins, and they must be continually replenished.

B-Complex Vitamins

Because all the B vitamins work in concert with one another, I am going to cover them as a family. When there is a deficiency of any one of the B vitamins, there is usually a shortage of the others as well.

The B-complex family consists of B1 (thiamine), B2 (riboflavin), B3 (niacin), B5 (pantothenic acid), B6 (pyridoxine), B12 (cyanocobalamin), B15 (pangamic acid), biotin, choline, folic acid, inositol and PABA (para-aminobenzoic acid).

The most important function of B-complex is its necessity during periods of pain, stress and dehydration. Other factors include: essential for mental and emotional health; provides energy; fights infection; maintains health of skin, hair, eyes, liver, nerves, muscles and digestive tract.

Deficiency of B-complex can cause poor

appetite, anemia, diarrhea, constipation, irritability, nervousness, depression, poor digestion, loss of vision, numbness and cramps in legs, heart and kidney problems.

Factors interfering with the absorption of B-complex include antibiotics, pesticides, sugar, cigarette smoke, vinegar, baking soda, laxatives, raw egg whites and synthetic hormones.

The best sources of B-complex are raw liver, green vegetables and whole grain cereals.

Brewers Yeast

I guess right here is the best place to talk about the overused and overrated "cure-all," brewers yeast. For years, probably ever since the first brewery, animals have been given yeast. Certainly there is no shortage of yeast, and it is cheap enough. So it is not surprising that it is the number one ingredient for every biscuit, commercial pet food and supplement known to animals.

The problem with brewers yeast is that carnivores cannot assimilate it because of their short intestinal tracts, and many have an intolerance and/or allergy to it.

About five years ago a series of cytotoxic tests were done on animals having skin allergies, and it was found that nine out of ten of them were allergic to yeast.

Kinesiology tests also showed an intolerance to brewers yeast.

In addition, because it is high in phosphorous it causes a calcium deficiency by throwing off the calcium-phosphorous balance within the system.

I don't think there's a person who hasn't tried massive amounts of brewers yeast on their animals to control fleas and excessive scratching. If brewers yeast were the answer to flea allergies, skin disorders and all the other conditions it is supposed to help, then why is it that 90 percent of our dogs and cats continue to have these problems?

For the past 20 years I have not given my own dogs and cats brewers yeast, nor have I recommended it to others.

What can you use instead? B complex vitamins, amino acids, minerals, aged and concentrated garlic, all of which provide the vitamins, amino acids and minerals found in yeast, and the above nutrients are easily absorbed by your animal's digestive system.

Vitamin C

The primary function of vitamin C is maintaining collagen, a protein necessary for the proper formation of connective tissue, ligaments, tendons, muscles, skin and bones.

As I have said over and over, nutrients work together as a family. If any one nutrient is out of balance—either too much or too little—the whole system suffers in one way or another.

Other functions of vitamin C that are just as important as producing collagen are: essential in the formation of adrenalin needed for stress; fights bacterial infections; protects other vitamins from oxidation; needed in forming red blood cells.

Deficiency of vitamin C can cause shortness of breath, upper respiratory infections, poor digestion, inflamed or bleeding gums, soft teeth, painful joints, anemia and slow healing of wounds and fractures.

Factors interfering with the absorption of vitamin C are cigarette smoke, stress, antibiotics, cortisone, exhaust fumes, sulfa drugs, baking soda and high fever. Drinking excessive amounts of water will wash vitamin

C and other nutrients right through the kidneys and out of the system. This is especially true in cats.

Dogs and cats produce approximately 40 milligrams a day of vitamin C. That is, of course, assuming they are in the peak of health. Maybe 2,000 years ago 40 mg of C was sufficient, but it certainly isn't now in our polluted environment.

According to most studies, and my own experience in using vitamin C, 1,500 mg to 8,000 mg per day (depending on the dog's size and condition) is my recommendation. Cats require 250 mg to 1,500 mg per day.

Again, let me remind you, the secret to giving vitamin C and other water soluble vitamins is giving small doses often, because C goes through the system in three to four hours.

For general maintenance, once or twice a day is sufficient. (When feeding fresh food your animal may be getting all he or she needs without giving supplements.)

If you are treating your cat or dog for a specific condition requiring vitamins B or C, you may have to give them several times a day. Kennel cough in dogs and upper respiratory infections in cats are two instances where I have had great success in using small amounts of vitamin C given several times a day.

Vitamin C stimulates the production of interferon and acts as an inactivator against viruses and bacteria. It is also essential for stimulating the immune system and enabling the body to resist diseases including cancer. Hip dysplasia is caused by a lack of vitamin C.

Probably the best form in which to take vitamin C, as with all vitamins, is the plant-cell grown C. (See Resources.)

It is also important to include some minerals in the formula rather than pure ascorbic acid or single ascorbates such as calcium ascorbate, because C by itself may cause the loss of valuable minerals such as potassium, calcium, magnesium, manganese, molybdenum, zinc and chromium, which are vitally needed because they transport the ascorbate through the cellular walls.

Here again is a situation where vitamins and minerals work synergistically.

Rich sources of vitamin C in a food form are kale, broccoli, alfalfa sprouts, citrus fruits, cantaloupe and strawberries.

Bioflavonoids - Vitamin P

Bioflavonoids, including hesperidin and rutin, are essential for the absorption of vitamin C. They are most plentiful in the white inner skin of citrus fruits.

Although fruits are not commonly fed to animals, they should be, if your animals like them.

Other sources of bioflavonoids are grapes, raisins, plums, currants, apricots, cherries, blackberries, rose hips and buckwheat.

Because bioflavonoids are so important to the support of vitamin C, and because cats and dogs do not often eat fruits and because animals, especially dogs, require even more bioflavonoids than people, I always suggest that whenever purchasing vitamin C make sure the mixture includes bioflavonoids. For every 1,000 mg of vitamin C there should be 500 mg of bioflavonoids.

Minerals

Minerals and vitamins work hand in hand. One is just as vital to the nutritional balance of the system as the other. Just recently minerals have again been given the credit they deserve.

All minerals, even the toxic ones, such as arsenic, cadmium and fluorine are necessary to maintain a healthy body. It is just that the toxic or poisonous minerals are needed in such minute amounts that just a little too much can be devastating, sometimes deadly, to the system.

That is why the safest way to provide minerals is through food and other natural elements, such as plant-cell-grown concentrates, herbs, bonemeal, algae, grasses, et al. In this way Mother Nature decides and provides the vitamins and minerals, even the toxic ones, in trace amounts, balanced and assimilable.

To reiterate, all vitamins, minerals, enzymes and bacteria are working in tandem to enable the system to produce the proper balance of nutrients for the body. One element cannot function without the other.

Calcium

Calcium is the most abundant mineral in the body. The majority of calcium in the body is utilized by the bones and teeth; however, it is also involved in the blood-clotting process, in nerve and muscle stimulation, parathyroid hormone functions and the metabolism of vitamin D. To function properly along with the high phosphorus content in meat, calcium must be accompanied by the proper supporting vitamins and minerals.

Magnesium is an essential mineral that must be present in a calcium formula for the body to properly absorb the calcium. In addition, it plays an important role in utilizing vitamins B, C and E. Studies point out that the balance between calcium and magnesium is especially important. The consensus now is that magnesium should be two-thirds of the amount of calcium in any formula.

From veterinarians and from authors of articles you hear about home-prepared meals for animals not being balanced. More often than not, that is true; not because people don't want to balance their cats' and dogs' meals, but because even the professionals who warn you that the meals are not balanced, don't take the time to tell you what IS balanced. In most cases that's because they either don't know or they are selling a commercial pet food that they want you to buy from them, and they want you to believe that preparing your own is too complicated.

There's nothing complicated about knowing that dogs and cats need raw meat and that meat is high in phosphorus, so you must balance it with an organic calcium plus the necessary nutrients for the body to utilize the calcium—it is mandatory.

The nutrients necessary for the proper absorption of calcium are: vitamins A, D, E, magnesium, boron, copper, molybdenum, potassium, sulphur and zinc.

The best available calcium complex is the organic food concentrate, Calcium+Plus. (See Resources.) With the organic food concentrates only small amounts are necessary because the potency is ten to fifteen times greater, as well as the fact that the body is able to utilize approximately 95 percent; whereas, bonemeal is utilized only 5 to 20 percent.

Bonemeal

Bonemeal has been the suggested form of calcium for years, until organic, plant-cell-grown calcium complex became available. Now there is no excuse for calcium deficiencies in animals, because the plant-cell-grown is so easy for animals to assimilate and utilize. (See Resources).

Bones

Raw bones are a necessary part of an animal's health. Chewing on them is healthy for the teeth, gums, jaws, as well as the nutrients. All bones are to be fed RAW!

When feeding chicken bones, only the necks and backs should be given, not wings or legs, because of the possibility of the wing and leg bones splintering and causing an internal puncture while going through the digestive system. Necks and backs do not splinter.

Raw beef or lamb knuckle bones and marrow bones are excellent as well. Be careful with marrow bones with animals that have slender lower jaws. If you get a marrow bone that is only about an inch long, the animal, after eating out the marrow, can get his/her jaw stuck in the center of the bone, caught over the bottom canine teeth, which may cause panic and injury. The answer is to get marrow bones that are at least three inches long so the animal cannot get her/his jaw caught.

Bones can be given as a treat, a dessert, instead of a meal, during fasting, or plain fun.

Calcium from calcium complex and from bones are ESSENTIAL. Three factors interfering with the absorption and utilization of calcium are cooked meat, sugar and chocolate.

Increasing Calcium Absorption

Thirty minutes of sunshine exposure each day is ideal to ensure adequate vitamin D for proper calcium absorption. Exercise your dog or cat regularly and moderately to halt calcium loss and increase bone mass. The bones need to exert force and bear weight against gravity to prevent loss of calcium. Increased calcium is necessary during periods of growth, with age, for heart and vascular disease, bone disorders and most nervous system disorders.

Chocolate is a Poison

Chocolate contains theobromine which is a poison to both cats and dogs. If you have been giving chocolate on a regular basis, they may be addicted to it. You will need professional help taking them off because they may suffer severe withdrawal symptoms.

I have seen the extremes in theobromine poisoning in dogs. One case involved two dogs in a family who were given chocolate bars consistently, up to three or four a week. Both of these dogs had arthritis, cancer and heart problems, but continued to linger on. They were the sickest living dogs I have ever seen. The owner would not stop giving the chocolate so there was no way I could help.

The other extreme was a dog who got into a box of chocolates and died within a couple of hours after eating approximately a half a pound.

It appears it is up to each individual system as to how much can be tolerated.

Fortunately, cats tend to be such fastidious eaters that unless encouraged as a kitten, they will usually not even eat chocolate.

Copper

Copper is not talked about often, but is an important trace mineral, especially for dogs. Many of copper's functions have to do with the assimilation of amino acids and fatty acids for proper muscle and bone formation. The best sources, in addition to bonemeal, are fish and green leafy vegetables.

Iodine

Iodine is very important to the thyroid gland, which controls the rate of metabolism, helping the body to maintain its proper weight.

More and more animals are on synthetic thyroid medication. It saddens me to see this type of treatment when something so simple and inexpensive as kelp (very rich in iodine) and fresh food could be an easy solution.

Iodine is vital in providing growth, energy and proper metabolism. Teeth, nails, skin and hair all depend on a healthy thyroid gland.

If your animal is already on a synthetic thyroid medication—which causes the thyroid to cease functioning and the animal to become completely dependent on the drug—consider supportive supplements and/or glandulars which will strengthen and heal the thyroid gland so it can function on its own again. You will need professional help to change from thyroid medication to glandulars.

When your animal gets on the fresh food program the thyroid gland is often stimulated and will begin to function again. Be sure to mention the change in diet to your health practitioner so he or she will be aware of this when giving the animal a blood test to check the activity of the thyroid.

Thyroid Imbalances

Thyroid imbalances are widespread in companion animals. Hypothyroidism is usual in dogs and hyperthyroidism is common in cats. Some veterinarians blame the frequent use of combination vaccines, a steady diet of complex carbohydrates (commercial pet foods) and cortisone drugs for these conditions.

Hypothyroid dogs often have a dry-looking coat with greasy-feeling skin that has a distinct odor and sticks to your fingers when you touch it. They typically have low energy and sometimes a groin rash that looks like tiny black dots. Hyperthyroid cats often lose weight despite a normal appetite and become nervous and irritable. They may be hyperactive for a few days, and then become lethargic, apathetic and unresponsive to eating, playing or grooming.

To help prevent thyroid problems, feed a well-balanced natural, raw diet and organic supplements and give your animal ample exposure to direct natural light (not through windows), because malillumination is a contributing cause of all glandular problems. If a thyroid problem exists, the proper herbs, glandulars and homeopathic remedies may be needed. Be sure to consult with a professional classical homeopathic practitioner for assistance.

Iron

Iron builds good, red blood. Raw meats are the best source, especially liver and heart. Leafy green vegetables, whole grains, raisins and molasses are also rich in iron.

General symptoms of iron-deficient anemia include weakness, lethargy, paleness (check the gums) and loss of appetite.

Here again, it is possible to be getting enough iron and anemia can still occur because of the lack of other nutrients necessary for absorption. Vitamin C is particularly important. Also, the amount of gastric acid regulates the solubility of iron. To repeat, dogs and cats must maintain high acidity—promoted by raw meat —to handle vital minerals like calcium and iron.

Magnesium

The cooking of food destroys magnesium. As long as carnivores are fed raw foods there will be sufficient magnesium.

This mineral is needed to help the body utilize vitamins B, C and E. It is a necessary element for bones, teeth, nerves, muscles and the conversion of blood sugar to energy.

Symptoms of magnesium deficiency include irritability, muscle twitching (often during sleep) convulsions, irregular heartbeat and kidney and bladder stones.

Magnesium is plentiful in fresh raw vegetables, grains, seeds and nuts. There is no reason for a magnesium deficiency if you are feeding raw foods.

Manganese

Not as well-known as magnesium, and often confused with it, manganese is of special importance to carnivores because it is a catalyst in the assimilation of fatty acids. It is also an enzyme activator. Without enzymes and their activators food cannot be digested.

Manganese is found in virtually the same foods as magnesium. One of the best sources is raw egg yolks.

Molybdenum

Molybdenum, a trace mineral, rates a mention because of its importance to the body in the utilization of fatty acids, iron and copper. Food sources of molybdenum include raw meats, legumes, and dark-green leafy vegetables.

Phosphorous

The importance of phosphorous-calcium balance is well-known in the nutrition world. Because phosphorous is easily absorbed by the system, it is usually not the lack of phosphorous that is the problem but the balance with calcium and other nutrients, especially vitamins B2, B3 and D.

The worst destroyer of the calcium-phosphorous balance is sugar, which is found in some form or another in most canned, moist and dry pet foods.

The important functions of phosphorous are bone growth, teeth development, kidney functioning and breaking up of fats, to name a few.

Raw meat, eggs, whole grains, seeds and nuts are all rich in phosphorous.

Potassium

Potassium's greatest value to your animal's system is normal growth. That seems over-simplified; however, insufficient potassium can cause muscle damage, especially to the heart. Another function is to keep sodium from getting out of line. With the overuse and abuse of salt in commercial foods, this is a big job.

An animal loses potassium and retains sodium when given steroids. Yet cortisone in the form of prednisolone or prednisone is given by traditional medical practitioners on a regular

---

Potassium

Potassium is a significant body mineral, important to both cellular and electrical function. It regulates the water balance and the acid-base balance in the blood and tissues. While any mineral deficiency can interfere with vitamin absorption, digestion and the health of every body system, a potassium deficiency can effect everything thing from the brain's electrical circuitry to the operation of the heart, circulatory system, reproductive organs, skeleton, skin and/or the lungs. A lifetime of problems can be prevented by feeding puppies and kittens the proper balance of minerals they need as their bodies grow.

Organ meats provide substantial iron and potassium. Leafy greens such as spinach, parsley, lettuce, and broccoli, all have significant levels of potassium. Fruits that contain this mineral include bananas, apples, avocados, raisins, and apricots. Sprouted grains are also high-potassium foods. Fish such as flounder, salmon, sardines, and cod are rich in potassium; as do many types of meat contain potassium.

---

basis for any medical problem that comes along when natural remedies would serve even better. Frightening, isn't it?

Potassium is also busy regulating fluids in the system. Dehydration can be swift and deadly. Proper water balance is of the utmost importance because water is the most abundant and important nutrient in any living being. Animals suffering from digestive disorders and diabetes are often potassium deficient.

The fresh food program will provide all the potassium necessary from the fish, meat, squash and yams.

Selenium

About ten, fifteen years ago it was trendy to talk about selenium deficiency. It is true that the amount of selenium in our food depends on the extent of its presence in the soil. However, as with other vitamins and minerals it is also depleted by cooking and processing food.

Selenium is one of the minerals that can do much harm if there is too much or too little. For instance, too little causes loss of hair and too much causes the same symptom. That's one of the reasons I'm concerned when supplemental selenium is given. How do you know when it's too much or too little?

Here again, let Mother Nature and the animal's body figure it out by feeding fresh raw food and letting them decide how much selenium is needed.

Montmorillonite clay, asparagus and garlic are chock-full of selenium.

Silica

A large proportion of the earth's crust is composed of this inorganic salt and yet not much is understood about its nutritional qualities and how it functions in the body.

We do know that it is a vital factor in the health of connective tissues, such as tendons, cartilage and blood vessels.

It also enhances calcium to produce strong bones.

Sodium

Yes, sodium or salt is an essential mineral necessary for water balance, equalizing potassium, assimilating calcium and other important functions in the body.

It is just that we have overused and abused it. Many of us, including our animals, like the taste.

The chance of there ever being a deficiency is slim to none. In addition to sodium being found naturally in just about every food, commercial food manufacturers and individuals always seem to add additional salt.

Excess salt causes loss of potassium, water retention, high blood pressure, and interferes with the assimilation of proteins.

Sulphur

If your dogs or cats are deficient in sulphur, they will have a flea problem.

Sulphur is one element that is present (or should be) in every cell of your animals' body. It is essential in producing collagen, keratin, insulin and other substances necessary for healthy skin, hair and nails.

The best nutritional sources of sulphur are garlic, eggs and raw meat.

Zinc

Two situations which almost always result from a zinc deficiency are cataracts and prostate problems. Oftentimes it is a factor in hip dysplasia as well.

Zinc is involved in every nutritional function from assisting vitamins, minerals and enzymes to proper development of reproductive organs. It is essential for a healthy skin and coat.

Reasons for a zinc deficiency are an unbalanced diet, taking cortisone or synthetic hormones.

Meat, fish, egg yolks, lecithin and, interestingly enough, pumpkin seed meal (which is an important ingredient for deworming) are rich sources of zinc.

FOOD-GROWN VITAMINS & MINERALS

In food, all vitamins and minerals are molecularly bound to a protein molecule which acts as the nutrient's natural carrier in living systems. There is no known exception to this natural law. Yet almost without exception, all vitamin and mineral supplements are in the form of isolates. This means that they lack their natural protein and carbohydrate bonds that occur in food.

Food-grown nutrients represent an entirely new class of supplements that not only have their natural protein and carbohydrate bonds, they contain every mineral and trace element known to exist in the food chain, as well as proanthocyanadins, a class of bioflavonoids from seeds and skin of grapes that are the most potent group of antioxidants known.

These antioxidants, minerals and trace elements also have their natural protein and carbohydrate bonds. These are not blended; they are grown. Merely blending a source of proteins and carbohydrates with vitamin and mineral molecules is not sufficient to create a result consistent with the complexity of nature's wise design.

Only growing them does, and nature does that with such complexity that we may never know the extent of this elaborate design or develop the ability to even understand it.

Beginning with the premise that Mother Nature knows best and that the complexity of nature's design fulfills a purpose that supports health, even if we don't understand the intricacies of how, if nature included something, it must be important. The tendency to fragment nature's holistic design, and the influence of this upon modern life has drastically altered animals' and people's ability to be adequately nourished.

Whenever possible, it is always better to take nutrients that are just as Mother Nature intended. These nutrients are now available to animals. See our Resources section for information on where to obtain them.

CHAPTER 9

MOTHER NATURE'S SUPPLEMENTS

Aloe Vera

If there is only one natural product you have in your home it should be aloe vera. Mother Nature has done it again by providing an inexpensive, all-encompassing, natural substance that heals everything from abrasions to zoonosis.

Aloe Vera

Known for centuries as the miracle plant or the potted physician, this cactus-like succulent with green dagger-shaped leaves filled with a clear, thick gel was first brought to North America from Africa in the sixteenth century. It is a member of the lily family.

Aloe, whose name means shining bitter substance, was once widely regarded as a truly special gift from the gods. The ancient Egyptians referred to aloe as the "plant of immortality" and buried it among the funerary gifts with the pharaohs. In recent decades, medical research has confirmed and extended many of the health claims associated with Aloe's internal and external use.

Aloe provides 200 or more nutrients, including vitamins, minerals, amino acids, steroids and organic acids, magnesium lactate, anthraglycosides, resins, mannis, enzymes, protein, wound-healing hormones, biogenic stimulators, saponins, lignins mucopoly-saccharides and mucopoly-saccharides, just to name a few. Applied to burns, aloe takes the heat out. It also acts as an anesthetic and has antibacterial and antifungal properties. Aloe vera juice can be effective for treating inflammatory bowel disease, according to a study in the *Journal of Alternative Medicine*. Aloe vera juice helps to detoxify the bowel, relieve constipation and gastric ulcers.

The most convenient form is aloe vera juice, however concentrate is preferable. Be sure there are no flavorings. Certified organic is another plus. Thickening agents in aloe vera such as Irish moss (which is an herb) or other natural sources are used if it is in gel form.

Aloe vera must contain a preservative to stabilize the aloe and to control bacteria. The preservative should be some form of vitamin C. The label may say citric acid, ascorbic acid or vitamin C, which, of course, are all one and the same.

Potassium sorbate, a mold inhibitor, is often added as well. Even with the natural preservatives, aloe vera must be refrigerated after opening.

Cat guardians, beware. Some brands of aloe are preserved with sodium bensoate or benzoic acid which is a known poison to cats. (Other products specifically for animals, contain sodium benzoate, so beware.)

Aloe vera is not standardized. They all say they are 99 percent pure aloe. The difference is in the processing; what process is used and what is left in or taken out. Most aloes in the health food stores are manufactured with taste in mind because people are going to drink them. Animals are not as concerned about palatability, so the brands I suggest are those that leave all the nutrients and oils in the aloe vera. (See Resource section.)

If you have your own aloe vera plants, by all means use them. However, keep in mind that they must be mature plants, meaning they are old enough to have developed the necessary medicinal properties. (There are over 200 different species and each has its own specificities.) Also, aloe that has not been stabilized will lose its effectiveness within a few hours.

For external use of your own aloe plants, peel off the skin from the leaves and rub the aloe flesh on your animal.

To prepare aloe for internal use you must peel the leaves, put the flesh of the aloe through a blender and use the liquid within four hours of picking. Even during the four-hour period it should be refrigerated.

Aloe vera concentrate (See Resources) should be added to every meal in the following proportions. Kittens and small cats, one teaspoon; cats, puppies and tiny dogs, two teaspoons, large puppies and small dogs, one tablespoon; dogs 20-40 pounds, two tablespoons; 40-60 pounds, three tablespoons; 60-80 pounds, four tablespoons; over 100 pounds, six tablespoons.

Internally aloe vera is excellent for allergies, arthritis, colitis, constipation, diarrhea, dental problems, hairballs, indigestion, liver and kidney disease, overweight or underweight, viral infections, yeast infections, and I'm sure I haven't thought of them all.

Any type of skin or coat problem: cuts, burns, insect bites, fleas, bruises, abrasions, poison ivy, welts, eczema, sunburn, hot spots, ulcerated skin lesions, ringworm, lick granulomas and greasy, dirty, dry, dull or sparse coat.

Aloe/H2O2: Aloe vera with food-grade hydrogen peroxide. For every two ounces of aloe vera concentrate add one teaspoon of 3 percent food grade hydrogen peroxide. This combination can be put in a spray bottle, a squirt bottle or just dabbed gently on the skin with gauze or a wash cloth.

Aloe/H2O2 works well for ear mites, infections or wax buildup. Squirt Aloe/H2O2 into each ear canal until you can see that each ear is completely full. Then gently massage the ears for one or two minutes. When you stop massaging, your animal will shake his or her head vigorously and ear gunk should go flying everywhere.

If the Aloe/H2O2 solution should get in the eyes, it may sting for a moment, but will not cause any harm.

Aloe/Calendula. Calendula is a homeopathic remedy made from marigold flowers that is particularly effective on open wounds and itchy areas where an animal has scratched the skin until it is red, raw and/or bleeding. For every two ounces of aloe vera concentrate add one teaspoon of calendular tincture.

The Aloe/Calendula combination can be used by itself or alternately with the Aloe/H2O2 solution in the same way as described above by putting it in a spray bottle, squirt bottle or patting it on the areas with gauze.

The only time aloe should not be given is during the first month of pregnancy because of its detoxification properties. During that time there is a natural detoxification by the body and to add to it is often overwhelming to the system.

Colostrum

Colostrum is a natural food—Mother Nature's first food—taken by babies, puppies and kittens. It would be hard to imagine any nutritional substance more beneficial.

Colostrum is not just for newborns. It contains many important growth factors which promote healing and actually create an anti-aging response. Independent medical studies show that colostrum's growth factors:

1) Regenerate and accelerate normal growth of aged or injured muscle, bone, cartilage, skin collagen and nerve tissue
2) Help burn fat for fuel instead of muscle tissue
3) Help build and retain lean muscle
4) Repair the body's vital DNA and RNA
5) Balance and regulate blood sugar levels
6) Heal burns, surgeries, cuts, abrasions, ear infections and mouth sores with topical application
7) Control infection and pain associated with gingivitis and sensitive teeth
8) Stop leaky gut syndrome and colitis
9) Balances brain chemical levels.

Colostrum contains immuno-regulatory factors (Immunoglobulins, Lactoferrin,

Cytokines and Interferon) as well as PRP (Polyproline-Rich-Peptides), which enhance the immune reaction when it is too low and suppress it when it is too high. This is important during those times when the immune system is extremely depressed, as in severe bacterial, viral, fungal infections, poor diet and vaccinations. It is also true in cases where the immune response is generally excessive in inflammation and destruction as in rheumatoid arthritis, lupus, multiple sclerosis, Chronic Fatigue Syndrome, Alzheimer's disease, allergies, etc.

An allergic reaction may manifest as watery eyes, runny nose, sinus stuffiness, asthma, hives, eczema, hot spots, rashes, high blood pressure, abnormal fatigue, abnormal hunger, stomach cramps, vomiting, anxiety, depression, aggressiveness, constipation, hyperactivity, wheezing, etc.

If your animal's immune system is healthy, s/he will not have allergies. Stress and adrenal exhaustion, poor diet, deficiency of vitamins B and C, poor elimination, emotional trauma, infections and vaccinations can weaken the immune system making one more susceptible to an allergic reaction.

Infants, puppies and kittens who are breast-fed have a lower frequency of allergic, inflammatory and autoimmune diseases and lymphomas, not only during nursing, but in their later life as well.

Most infectious microorganisms enter the body through the mouth and are swallowed. How well we know with children, cats and dogs. Everything goes in the mouth! Whether or not one can defend themselves against these invaders which surround all of us depends on the health of the immune system. Normally the immune system is able to properly fight these off. Some people and animals are not so lucky. It seems they catch every bacterium, virus and fungus that comes their way.

MDs and DVMs have gotten into the unforgivable habit of prescribing antibiotics for everything that enters the office. Between 80-90 percent of these ailments are caused by viral infections and an antibiotic is not going to do any good. Antibiotics are harmful in that they are responsible for creating new and unusual challenges for the immune system.

Antibiotics, vaccines and other drugs disrupt the normal harmonious relationship in the body. Antibiotics destroy beneficial bacteria, can cause indigestion, yeast infections, ear infections, allergic reactions, even death.

Colostrum, as well as other natural antibiotics, offers safe viral and bacterial protection. Dozens of scientific papers suggest that colostrum can block or reduce the severity of a wide variety of infections including many of which have their initiation in the oral/fecal route. Colostrum is effective against a number of microorganisms including E coli, streptococcus, salmonella, bordetella, respiratory viruses, yeasts such as candida, to name a few. Colostrum can be used as a safe, effective alternative to antibiotics, steroids and vaccines.

Colostrum contains IGF-1, the most powerful growth factor in the body. Medical research has shown that without adequate amounts of IGF-1, the body, during times of fasting or dieting, will burn muscle protein before they burn fat (catabolism). The only means to increase IGF-1 levels in the body is through daily aerobic exercise or colostrum (preferably both). The IGR-1 and other growth factors in colostrum help burn fat and build lean muscle mass.

How To Take Colostrum

If you want to concentrate on the growth factors (including metabolizing or burning fat, building muscle and accelerating healing) you should take or give colostrum in powder form so that it has maximum opportunity to interact with natural concentrations of stomach acid.

On the other hand, the effectiveness of the immune factors present in colostrum is lowered by stomach acid. The immune components are most effective when they are able to reach the intestinal tract. Therefore, the best way to ensure that colostrum's immune factors remain intact and make it through the stomach to the intestinal tract is to take colostrum in capsule form.

If you want to get the benefits of the two different major groups of components in colostrum, ideally you should take it in two different forms—in powder to take advantage of its growth factors and in capsule form to get the maximum benefit from its immune factors.

Colostrum works best on an empty stomach. Do not take any other supplements at the same time that you take colostrum and wait at least twenty minutes before eating. It has a pleasant taste (similar to skim milk) so the powder can be placed right on your animal's tongue, and you can do the same for yourself. Drinking water afterwards is very beneficial. If you have to put it in food for your animal, mix it in a little yogurt or butter, just enough to get them to take it.

Each animal and each person is unique with regard to the amount of colostrum they need. Start with the suggested use on the bottle label.

Colostrum can be consumed in any quantity without side effects or drug interactions. Because colostrum helps heal the bowel, this means you are better utilizing the nutrients from the food you eat and the supplements and medications you take. This can reduce or even eliminate the need for many additional supplements and medications. Consult with your healthcare provider for advice and re-evaluation of your supplements and/or medication needs. Those who are lactose-intolerant should have no problems with high quality colostrum.

Why Drugs Don't Work

Animals on antibiotics, antihistamines, hormones or cortisone appear not to have problems for awhile, because drugs suppress disease. Then when you discontinue the drugs, the ailment always comes back and every time it comes back it is even worse than before. If you continue with the drugs, the amount taken has to be increased on a regular basis as the body gets used to the drug. In addition, the side effects of drugs can often be more deadly than the disease.

Natural Detoxification

Whatever your animal encounters in the way of detoxification, there is a natural way to take care of it. Organic supplements, neutriceuticals and homeopathic remedies can be given to help the body detox.

Natural remedies that can be used internally for detoxification problems are organic food supplements, FHES (Silica Hydride), MSM (organic sulphur), colostrum, grapefruit seed extract, colloidal silver, PuriZone+Plus, essential fatty acids and aloe vera, to name a few.

Only products that are edible should be put on your dog topically, because everything that's put on the outside goes inside when they groom themselves. (See Chapter 15 on external products.)

Natural Antibiotics

The majority of the bacteria in our system is friendly. We need these good guys to digest food, to prevent infections, to control the bad guys and for a myriad of other functions necessary to life.

Synthetic antibiotics used in orthodox medicine have only two functions: to halt bacterial growth or to outright kill all bacteria. They do not discriminate between the good guys and the bad guys.

Allopathic medicine is overly and unnecessarily aggressive. Drugs that kill are not the answer.

Synthetic antibiotics are arbitrarily given by conventional practitioners whether the animal is suffering from a bacterial or viral infection. If it's viral, antibiotics have no effect and, if it's bacterial, the condition is only complicated by destroying the friendly bacteria which are necessary for healing.

Natural antibiotics can be given safely by you or by a health practitioner without the side effects of synthetic antibiotics. The world is full of natural substances; Mother Nature would never let us down.

She has given us garlic that has a similar

antibiotic action as penicillin; goldenseal which has strong antibiotic properties similar to tetracycline and streptomycin; echinacea, best known for its cleansing abilities for the lymphatic system; aloe vera, recognized as a healer of all types of skin problems, allergies, stomach and colon disorders; grapefruit seed extract which stops the growth of many fungi and bacteria, such as candida, streptococcus and salmonella, excellent for sore throats and ear infections; colloidal silver, a pure mineral supplement, which is highly germicidal and absolutely non-toxic. It is tasteless and odorless, so it may be taken orally, inhaled into the nose, dropped into the eyes or applied directly to the skin, and bee propolis, an excellent aid against bacterial infection by stimulating phagocytosis (the ingestion and destruction of unfriendly bacteria by white blood cells).

PROBIOTICS

In addition to natural antibiotics, and instead of the synthetics, a positive approach is to use probiotics (friendly bacteria), to overcome the unfriendly.

Intestinal flora, beneficial bacteria, probiotics, are all names for microorganisms which are an essential part of the functioning of the entire gastrointestinal tract.

They protect the body against pathogenic or harmful foreign invaders, maintain vital chemical balance, produce needed vitamins and hormones and an array of other essential tasks necessary to maintain proper growth and a healthy immune system.

Inadequate levels of beneficial intestinal flora are directly associated with the following conditions: skin problems, osteoporosis, gas, diarrhea, constipation, bladder and yeast infections, high cholesterol, vitamin B deficiency, anemia, allergies and bad breath.

If your animal is suffering from any of the above, I would highly recommend adding probiotics to the raw food.

Out of several hundred different species of beneficial bacteria living in the intestine, five that are of particular importance are: lactobacillus acidophilus, bifidobacterium bifidum, lactobacillus casei, streptococcus faecium and lactobacillus salivarius. (See Resources.)

FOS

Fructooligosaccharides (FOS), a natural carbohydrate that dramatically increases the number of friendly intestinal bacteria, is an excellent addition to probiotics, because it selectively encourages the proliferation of bacterial groups that are beneficial, such as bifidobacteria and lactobacilli.

Studies show that after two weeks the bifidobacteria increases by an average of forty-fold and lactobacilli increased seven-fold. By acting like a "fertilizer," FOS enhances the growth and improves the balance of intestinal flora. In addition, FOS suppresses the production of toxins, promotes peristalsis and improves bowel function.

Probiotics provide friendly bacteria; whereas, antibiotics indiscriminately kill both the good and bad bacteria. Whenever we have the choice of building or destroying the choice seems obvious.

The more we incorporate Mother Nature's supplements into our food, our healing and our lives in general, the better it will be for our animals and for us.

Willie's Saga

I started Willie on a full raw food diet in July 2001. Soon afterwards he was looking great, stopped smelling so bad and he put on some needed weight. His ears that had always had heavy black waxy discharge since he was a rescued kitten were clearing up.

About 2-3 weeks later he started drooling on one side of his mouth. After he continued to drool for another week I took him into Pat McKay's and Pat said he looked like he might have a tumor or an abscess and recommended that I see a vet/surgeon.

The vet took a look at his mouth and immediately said he believed that my cat had mouth cancer and that in order to save the cat I would have to remove the cat's lower jaw. (1/3 of his face). I asked if there was any possibility that it wasn't cancer. He said in his experience the kind of tumor Willie had was almost guaranteed to be cancer. He recommended that I have a biopsy taken if I wanted confirmation.

I decided that the operation was not an option. I had seen a cat that had the operation and he was unhappy, couldn't eat properly and had this gaping hole on the bottom of his face. He couldn't keep himself properly hydrated since he could hardly drink water. I went back to consult with Pat McKay. Willie was put on 12 drops of Cansema Tonic mixed with an equal amount of water and 1/8 tsp C+ Plus administered daily. He was also given A+ Plus, Calcium+ Plus, C+ Plus, Revive, ProEnergy, CoQ10, FHES and PuriZone+ Plus (to keep his system clean) mixed with his food, plus Colostrum (mixed with butter so he would eat it). The drooling went from constant to occasional in the first two weeks; it stopped completely two weeks later. The tumor stopped growing; it seemed to remain static for about a month and then the second month it started to get smaller. The visible area in his mouth near his lips started out at about the size of a kidney bean, plus other parts of the tumor wrapped his jawbone causing him to drool and making his face asymmetrical. After three months the tumor was about 1/2 its original size.

Throughout the treatment my cat has been healthy, playful, had a great appetite and appears to be in beautiful condition. As of February 14, 2002, I have had Willie's mouth and health checked every 3 weeks since the tumor disappeared on November 7, 2001. There is no sign of any tumor.

Sincerely, Ed Skaats
skaats@earthlink.net

CHAPTER 10

THE TEN-MINUTE MEAL

Now that you are familiar with the basic food groups and the supplements, the actual preparation of the meal should take ten minutes or less.

For the first few days, until you get organized and comfortable with the preparation, it may take longer. However, if after a week or so you are taking more than ten minutes per animal to prepare their meals you either love to be in the kitchen or you are being too particular about putting it all together.

DO-IT-YOURSELF HOMEMADE BASIC RECIPE: FOR BOTH CATS & DOGS

75% raw, ground meats and
25% raw, ground vegetables

Yields 1 cup of food.
   3/4 cup ground raw meat, poultry or fish
   4 tablespoons raw, ground, mixed vegetables
   1/4 cup purified water
   (See supplement information below)

Yields 3 cups of food
   1 pound ground, raw meat, poultry or fish
   1/2 cup raw, ground, mixed vegetables
   1/2 cup purified water
   (See supplement information below)

Yields 9 cups of food
   3 pounds ground, raw meat, poultry or fish
   $1^1/_2$ cup raw, ground, mixed vegetables
   $1^1/_2$ cups of purified water
(See supplement information below)

Adding Supplements

Calcium+Plus, a calcium complex, MUST be added to all the above raw food recipes. In the wild, canines and felines eat the entire animal, bones and all. We need to provide a meal that is as close to Mother Nature's design as possible. Meat is very high in phosphorus, and to meet the proper calcium/phosphorus ratio, calcium MUST be supplemented at every meal.

AnimaLife, an organic, plant-cell-grown vitamin/mineral complex provides a complete balance of all essential vitamins and minerals.

Specific products such as aloe, enzymes, probiotics, essential fatty acids or whatever nutrients are necessary for your animal's individual needs are to be added at this time also.

(See our Resource section, page 173, for specific information on these supplements.)

Mix all the above ingredients well. Keep adding purified water until the food is the consistency of thick, thick chili. If you can form a meatball with the mixture, you need more water. You want the food to be fully saturated with water without being like soup. This is the most efficient way for carnivores to assimilate water.

Quantity of Food

If your animals have been used to eating one meal a day or two meals a day, keep them on the same schedule when first introducing raw food.

If they have been free feeding, that must come to a halt. Carnivores' digestive systems and organs must have a complete rest for several hours at a time.

For adult dogs and cats, one meal a day is best, if they are healthy. In fact, some adult animals on the Pat McKay raw food program voluntarily eat every second or third day rather than everyday because they are nutritionally satisfied

Puppies and kittens should have anywhere from three to six meals a day. For all dogs and cats, whether they are overweight, underweight, sick, healthy, young or old, put so much food in the bowl or plate every day (every meal for puppies and kittens) that they walk away with some food left over. They must eat until THEY have decided they have eaten all they want.

If you had ten dogs or cats all the same breed, same size, same gender, same color, they would each need and want a different amount of food on any given day.

The decision of quantity is not up to you. This is one decision your animals must make all on their own.

Overweight animals will lose weight on this program because they will stop eating when their bodies are nutritionally satiated.

Underweight animals will gain weight and the sick will get well because they are finally getting the nutrients they need.

Of course, there are always exceptions to the rule. Consult your animal practitioner for specific ailments, such as problems caused from glandular dysfunction (thyroid, pancreas), diabetes, etc. Sick animals may have to eat more often.

Ground Beef At Your Local Market

If meat is ground and packaged at a USDA-inspected plant beef fat may be added to "hamburger," but not "ground beef." A maximum of 22% fat by weight is allowed. Both hamburger and ground beef may have seasonings, but no water, phosphates, extenders or binders added. They must be labeled in accordance with Federal Standards and Labeling Policy and marked with a USDA-inspected label.

Most ground beef is ground and packaged in local stores rather than in food processing plants. Most states and cities set standards for store-packaged ground beef. If products in retail stores were found to contain more than 22% fat by weight, they would be considered "adulterated" under Federal law. The larger cuts are usually shipped to local stores where they are ground. The Food Safety and Inspection Service carries out USDA's Responsibilities under the Federal Meat Inspection Act. These laws protect consumers by ensuring that meat products are wholesome, unadulterated, and properly marked, labeled, and packaged.

Ground Meat Versus Chunks

Ideally it would be better to feed meat in large chunks so our animals could rip and tear at the meat as they would their prey in the wild. The problem is that most carnivores will pick out the meat and leave the vegetables.

My suggestion is to feed ground meat thoroughly mixed with vegetables and occasionally feed chunks of meat.

Also, a knuckle bone with a lot of meat still on it is an excellent choice.

It is easier on the animal's digestive system to feed one protein at a time. In other words, at the meal that you feed beef, feed only beef. It is better not to mix eggs, chicken or other meats in that meal.

If you happen to have some leftovers from the previous meal and it is a different protein, it's not the end of the world. You can feed the leftovers. I don't mean for you to be a purist about the fresh food program or to waste good food. But don't purposely mix proteins.

Combining Vegetables

Just the opposite is true of vegetables. It is best to feed several vegetables at each meal. They act synergistically by enhancing the nutritional value when combined.

Rotating Foods

It is essential to rotate all foods. Do not feed the same meats or vegetables day after day. Each food has its own particular molecular chain and specific valuable nutrients to offer the system.

For instance, broccoli and cabbage may be of the same family, but each has its own unique combinations of nutrients to offer.

It is vitally important that the body has the opportunity to use whatever nutrients it needs at any given time. The best way to do that is to give the body a variety. It will know which nutrient it needs and when.

Here again, let Mother Nature do the tough part, deciding what the body needs and when it needs it.

Another reason for rotating is that it is important that the animal does not get hooked on any one particular taste. Sometimes, as many of us already know, these habits are hard to break. We all have our favorites, and that's okay, but variety is necessary for proper nutritional balance and is not to be overlooked. No matter how good something is or how well balanced, if you eat the same foods repeatedly, the body is going to build up a resistance, intolerance or allergy to those ingredients. Give your animal the benefit of a well-rounded menu by varying their meals.

How Much Does It Cost?

Commercial canned and dry pet food ranges in price from 3.6 cents per ounce to 22.9 cents per ounce. The fresh, raw, whole food costs approximately 3.5 cents per ounce for dogs and 5 cents per ounce for cats.

The following will summarize what has already been covered in the first chapters concerning the fresh, RAW food program:

Meats, Poultry & Fish

Organic, naturally grown or free-range meat is the best, of course. However, depending what part of the country you live in, good meats are sometimes hard to find. Check with your health food stores, independent meat markets and supermarkets and get the best you can find. (See Resources.)

Be sure to get meat that is high in fat content, 15 to 22 percent, or as high as 30 percent, which is the highest that can be sold. Remember organ meats have very little fat, so the overall fat content of the complete fresh, raw food program will be closer to 10 to 15 percent fat.

Meats to be given to your animals are beef, chicken, lamb, turkey, heart, kidney, liver, melts and gizzards. (No pork.)

Eggs are an excellent source of complete protein, especially if they come from organically raised chickens. Also, If you can find organically grown or naturally farmed fish, they are wonderful as well.

Concerns About Cat Litter

Clay and perfume (odor control) based cat litters are actually causing serious health problems in cats including asthma, bronchitis, constipation and possibly even lung cancer, according to recent reports by veterinarians.

Ordinary commercial litters are laden with chemicals to reduce odor and help with urine and stool absorption. These chemicals are inadvertently released into the air when your cat covers his waste in the litter box. The dust from the litter travels into the cat's lungs and wreaks havoc on his or her immune system, causing poor health, asthma, bronchitis or cancer. Harm can occur in just a short period of time.

Clay litters, which form a hard ball when they get wet, are some of the most harmful types of litter on the market. When the clay gets wet, it expands and forms a hard mass. So when your cat or kitten digs in the litter box it is kicking up clay dust and involuntarily breathing it in. Once it gets into their lungs, it can expand from the moisture and in time cause different lung related aliments.

There are actual warnings posted on the bags of some clay clumping litters, "Do Not Let Cat Ingest Litter." Good luck training your cat to stop breathing while in the litter box and not grooming himself afterwards. Once the clay litter is inside your cat and it expands, it not only could cause dehydration by absorbing the body's moisture, it could also form a hard mass in the intestines over a period of time, which could be fatal.

The solution is easy. Switch to a biodegradable, dust and clay free, clumping litter. Many of these biodegradable litters are made from recycled paper or food, like corn or wheat, which will help to save the environment as well as your cat. You can find these products almost anywhere. Just be sure to read the label.

Vegetables
Any and all of the following vegetables can be used. The more veggies you combine in one

meal the better. I have underlined the ones that I use on a daily basis.

Asparagus, beets, <u>broccoli,</u> Brussels sprouts, <u>cabbage,</u> <u>carrots,</u> <u>cauliflower,</u> celery, corn, dry beans (see page 29), green beans, <u>greens</u> (dandelion, kale, Swiss chard, parsley), kohlrabi, lentils (see page 38), okra, parsnips, peas, pumpkin, sprouts (alfalfa, bean, sunflower) <u>squash</u> (winter and summer varieties), <u>sweet</u> <u>potatoes,</u> turnips and rutabagas.

All vegetables must be put through the food processor or blender to be ground down to the size of the head of a straight pin or the size of salt or sand. Dogs and cats do not digest large chunks of vegetables easily.

Keeping Food Fresh

Fresh food, after it is mixed, will last approximately two to three days in the refrigerator. However, you may make up large batches of the food and freeze it in daily portions.

Adding Supplements

It is always best to add the supplements just before feeding, so the nutrients do not dissipate while sitting in the food in the refrigerator.

If you make the food in large batches and freeze it, do not add the supplements until just before feeding.

I repeat again: You MUST add a calcium complex. Calcium+Plus is recommended because it is organic and plant-cell-grown.

AnimaLife, an organic, plant-cell-grown vitamin/mineral complex is beneficial to cover all the necessary vitamins and minerals that are no longer available directly from food.

Optimally, the healthiest source of nutrition is naturally healthful food grown in nutrient rich soil without chemical intervention. Unfortunately, most foods no longer provide the necessary nutrients. Our soil is continually being depleted of the ingredients that would contribute to creating healthy plants and animals. Almost without exception, no remineralization is being done to compensate for the abuse or to replenish the life of the soil, thus the food grown is deficient and unhealthy.

Therefore, for all dogs and cats I highly recommend an organic vitamin/mineral complex like AnimaLife. (See Resources.)

More Bribery

You may always add more RAW meat, even if you are feeding only meat for a few days until they have accepted that part of the program. Remember, they are carnivores, and meat is the very essence of their nutritional needs.

If you have to cook (even though I don't like to use that four-letter word) a small portion of the meat because they are used to the smell and texture of cooked meat, that's okay as a bribery tactic.

Sometimes, if you make up a raw meat broth, they will drink that to begin with. For every one cup of purified water, you add two tablespoons of RAW ground meat and either mash it in the water with a fork or put it in a blender. This is also a wonderful solution for sick animals who are dehydrated.

For any additional help you may need, see the Resource section.

CHAPTER 11

DESSERTS

I know there are times when you just can't resist giving your dog or cat a dessert along with whatever you are having. If so, give your animal something healthy. They will enjoy the healthy desserts even more because they won't have an upset stomach afterwards.

For instance, when you are having ice cream give them yogurt or one of the ice creams made from rice or soy beans and sweetened with honey. Give healthy crackers, cookies or breads made for people (without salt or sugar). Give nut and seed milk (instead of dairy) from health food stores or make it yourself with the following recipe.

Nut and Seed Milk

1/2 cup sunflower seeds
1/4 cup walnuts
1/4 cup almonds
1 cup purified water

Blend in food processor or blender until a complete liquid.

Banana Pudding

1 block Tofu (10-12 ounces)
3 ripe bananas
1/2 cup maple syrup or molasses
1/2 cup vegetable oil
1 tablespoon lemon juice and/or vanilla
    Mix in blender or with electric mixer.

Rice Pudding

1 cup cooked brown rice
2 beaten eggs
2 tablespoons maple syrup or molasses
1/2 cup raisins
1/4 teaspoon cinnamon
    Mix all ingredients (add extra water, if necessary) and simmer for 20 minutes. Let cool and serve.

Sweet Potato Pudding

1 cup cooked mashed sweet potatoes
1/2 cup soy milk or nut and seed milk
1/3 cup vegetable oil
2 beaten eggs
1/2 cup honey
1 teaspoon ground nutmeg
    Combine all ingredients, blend well. Pour in a bowl and step aside so you don't get trampled in the rush.

Cookies

3 cups barley or rice flour
2 teaspoons Calcium+Plus
2 teaspoons of AnimaLife
2 egg yolks
2 tablespoons yogurt (Goat's milk is best)
1/3 cup molasses
1 tablespoon vegetable oil
2 tablespoons of 3% food grade $H2O2$
2 tablespoons of purified water

Mix dry ingredients well. Pour liquid ingredients in food processor. Blend for a few seconds. Add dry ingredients and mix until blended.

Roll out dough to whatever thickness is best for your animals. Very thin for cats; approximately 1/2 inch for medium dogs and 1 inch thick for large dogs. Cut with any cookie cutter and place on oiled cookie sheet.

Thin egg whites with water and brush tops of cookies.

Bake at 325 degrees for approximately 25 minutes for cat size; 40 minutes for medium dog size and 60 minutes for large dog size.

CHAPTER 12

INSTINCT

Many people believe that animals instinctively know what is good for them to eat. That may be true in the wild before their instincts have been distorted by humans, but after they are domesticated that is not necessarily the case.

Use Your Instincts

Does it make sense to feed commercial pet food when it has cattle and poultry parts deemed unfit for human consumption? Animals classified as 4D refers to dead, diseased, dying and disabled animals, including road kill, deceased zoo animals with antibiotic and pesticide residue, growth hormone implants, toenails, hooves and beaks. These rejected animal parts include cancerous tissues, worm-infested organs, contaminated blood and blood clots. Compounding these toxins, slaughterhouses add carbolic acid, black paint and fuel oil to these remnants as a way of marking these foods as unfit for human consumption as required by state law. These ingredients are what are called "meat meal" or "meat-by-products."

Even dry and canned foods labeled "human grade," are not any better for your dog or cat. These foods can be cooked up to an hour at 220° F to 270° F destroying vital enzymes and nutrients. Cooking meat also results in the proteins becoming indigestible and the fat turning into grease. Cat and dogs cannot assimilate grease whatsoever. When food is cooked, it retains sufficient nutrients to keep your dog or cat alive with no obvious immediate problems. It does not however, allow your animal to have a long, healthy, trouble-free life. Cooked food is responsible for much ill health in our companion animals including cancer, kidney disease, arthritis, pancreatic disease, and many more ailments.

Many times we confuse instincts and what mommadog or mommacat teaches their young. They are taught to stalk, hunt, kill and eat their prey. That isn't all instinctual.

When domesticated animals chase birds, mice and lizards, they don't always know they are supposed to be serious about this whole business. Most of the time they are just in it for the good time. If they do catch and kill their prey, they often don't eat it, because they were never told it is okay to do so.

Dogs and cats need to be encouraged to eat healthy foods.

Their sense of smell is their key to eating. If they are used to smelling canned or dry food, they believe that is what they are supposed to eat. Fresh meat does not have that strong, garbage-like smell.

I get calls and letters (especially from cat guardians) saying, "My animal won't eat the fresh food." Well, no wonder, if all the animal has eaten up to now are overcooked, devitalized foods filled with sugar, salt and other chemical enhancers.

If your two-year-old child had been eating hot dogs, potato chips, ice cream and candy all the time, it would certainly be no surprise to you that she would turn down a beautiful plate of vegetables. The same is true for your animals.

Bribe Foods

You may have to encourage them to eat good food. One way is to give bribe foods, such as liver, molasses, honey, grated cheese, sardines, cooked chicken or any food that your dog or cat just happens to like. Even if you have to mix some of the canned food they like, maybe half fresh food and half canned food, for awhile. Do whatever works to encourage them to eat the good fresh food. Then slowly increase the fresh food and decrease the bribe foods.

The Voluntary Fast

If you have a young, healthy cat, I would try the "voluntary" fast first. You put down the fresh food twice a day; he won't eat it; he volunteers to fast.

Your cat can easily go three or four days without eating, no problem. It may be a problem for you, because most guardians get pretty upset when their animals aren't eating.

If and when it bothers you, or if the cat becomes aggressive, lethargic or just plain unhappy, go to the bribe-food method.

If you have a cat or dog who is over seven years old or has any medical problems, do not do the voluntary fast. Start with the fresh food for one or two meals and see if he or she will eat it and, if not, try the bribe foods.

Do not put your animal or yourself through any trauma over changing to fresh foods. A little bribery or compromising will work just fine. Even if it takes days, weeks or months, what's the difference? You are at least going in the right direction.

Free Feeding

If you have been allowing your animals to free feed, stop.

Carnivores' digestive systems and organs must have a complete rest for several hours at a time.

If you want a companion animal that eats all the time, get a goat. They have four stomachs that must be kept busy at all times. Their digestive systems are the direct opposite of a carnivore's system.

Metabolism, Not Weight

Every dog and cat needs a different amount of food each time they eat, just as people do. It is how the body metabolizes the food that decides how much is necessary. How much are you going to eat at your next meal? Most people put more food on the table than is expected that everyone will eat and usually there are leftovers. That's how it should be for your animals.

Adult cats and dogs should be offered food once a day and allowed to eat all they want at that time. However, if just starting out increase the amount of food you give each day <u>until</u> your dog or cat walks away with food in their bowl or plate – that is the only way they have to tell us they are satisfied. Puppies and kittens should be fed on demand. They will let you know how many times a day they want to eat. They should get all they want to eat as often as they want from two to six times a day.

No Dry Food

Dry food was created for the convenience of the guardians and not for the well-being of the animals. Sure it's great to put down dry food and go away for several days, but what kind of food can sit for days on end and still have any nutritional value? Also, it becomes rancid (sometimes even before it leaves the manufacturing plant) and rancidity is one of the worst known carcinogens.

Cats were originally savanna animals and were meant to get 99 percent of their water from their food. Dry foods have only 2 percent water, so the cat's body must then pull the other 97 percent of much-needed moisture from their own systems to make up the difference. No wonder so many cats have kidney problems.

All cats that get feline urilogical syndrome (FUS)—sometimes referred to as cystitis or kidney/bladder stones—are cats that have been fed dry or canned food, (especially dry food).

You will hear all kinds of stories about cats getting FUS from too much ash, or too much magnesium, or whatever story the medical community and commercial food manufacturers are touting at the moment. But the truth is that cats get FUS from dry and canned foods, because all commercial foods are cooked and they do not contain sufficient water.

Cats not only do not get FUS when they eat raw, whole foods, but if your cat presently has FUS, the fresh food will clear up the problem.

Dry food is not good for dogs either. The only reason I make a point of talking about cats is that FUS is in such direct correlation with the dry food that it makes the point very clear. But I don't want to leave you with the impression that I condone dry foods for dogs or any animals.

Dry Food Does Not Clean Teeth

Another myth is that hard, dry food cleans teeth. There is no truth to that story either. Dogs' and cats' teeth are cleaned by the acid that comes up into their mouths just as they are about to eat.

When carnivores in the wild are stalking their prey, their digestive systems get ready for the food by producing highly acidic digestive juices.

In order to break down skin, bones, hair and meat of their prey, those juices need to be extremely powerful. When these acids come up into the mouth to break down the mouse or bird, they clean any plaque or tartar that may have accumulated on the teeth.

Raw—not cooked—meat stimulates these digestive juices. Plaque buildup can often be reduced within a few weeks just by eating the fresh food.

Bones, Cookies and Biscuits

Chewing on bones strengthens and massages the gums to keep them healthy as well as providing a proper balance of nutrients. Raw knuckle bones and soft cartilage bones are the only ones to give.

Do not give cooked bones of any kind. Do not give long bones that will splinter when your animal chomps down on them. Do not give bones that are small enough to fit inside your dog's or cat's mouth because they might swallow them.

Raw marrowbones must be 3 to 4 inches in length because there is the possibility of your animal's jaw being caught in the center of the bone when your cat or dog is working his/her tongue and jaw into the bone trying to get the marrow. I don't give rawhide, pigs ears or other treated chewies because they have been bleached with chemicals and held together with glue.

Cookies and biscuits made with honey or molasses are fine to give for their pleasure or yours. I'm not discouraging your giving treats and rewards, but the average cat cookie or dog biscuit on the market is just filled with junk.

Some nutritious cookies with rice or barley flour make fine treats. But if the cookies or biscuits are made specifically for animals, you really need to read the labels carefully. Most of them have very little nutritional value. I would also make sure they are fit for human consumption as well.

Feeding Leftovers

If you eat healthy fresh food that is steamed, boiled or baked, feel free to feed any leftovers to your animals.

If you personally eat fried, canned or fast-food meals filled with grease, salt, sugar, chemicals and fillers, that is certainly your right. You can make the choice. But remember your animal is captive and cannot make his or her own choice.

You have been given the honor and the privilege of sharing your life with this supreme sentient being. Your animal deserves healthy food.

Feeding Raw

Prior to World War II, people fed their dogs and cats butcher or slaughter scraps. Resuming to that way of feeding can be done easily and intelligently with today's use of nutritional knowledge. I cannot stress enough in order to have healthy dogs and cats DO NOT feed cooked foods, (all foods in a bag or a can are cooked, Rawhide is cooked, pig's ears are cooked, etc.). DO NOT feed vegetables in large chunks. Vegetables need to be broken up in order for your animal to digest and utilize them properly. Wash them well to remove any toxic chemicals before peeling them and put them through a blender to reduce them to pulp before feeding them to your dog or cat.

DO NOT feed fat trimmings only. This will cause a severe imbalance with your animal. Feed raw muscle meat, organ meat and raw bones. Raw meat and raw bones supply proteins, the essential fatty acids and many nutrients only available from raw foods.

Travel Foods

Traveling, vacations, earthquakes, hurricanes, long power failures, etc., present a dilemma of what to feed our animals, as well as ourselves, and still stay on a fresh food program.

First of all, your dogs and cats can eat the very same foods as you are eating as long as what you are eating is wholesome. Everyone should be eating good food because you and your animals are more vulnerable to health problems during stress.

Vacations are wonderful, but they are also a time of a change in lifestyle, even though pleasurable, and any change brings about a greater demand on our systems.

Some suggestions of foods that are simple and easy to find would be raw beef, lamb, chicken or turkey and all of the organ meats (ground or chunk), knuckle bones, marrow-bones, beef rib bones, eggs, fresh fruits and vegetables, frozen mixed vegetables, PhytoFoods (Healthy treats containing 36 superfoods); if you absolutely can't find raw foods you can give canned meats or fish, canned soups (no salt), yogurt (no sugar), almond butter or apple butter on rice cakes, sesame crackers or sprout bread.

Freeze-dried or dehydrated meats and vegetables are now available for animals, as well as people. I would recommend feeding them only when you absolutely have to because they do not rehydrate well and some animals have trouble digesting them.

Whenever you buy fresh, raw meats, buy just enough for one day and let your animal eat the meat all at once so you don't have a spoilage problem. The next day feed vegetables (if your animal will eat them separately). The body remembers. It isn't necessary to feed all food groups every day.

The point is that you want to feed foods that are fit for human consumption and are wholesome. As long as you stay away from sugar and salt you are pretty safe. Stock up in advance before you leave on your trip or keep a supply during bad weather seasons.

If you are eating in restaurants, order soft-boiled eggs or baked chicken or fish or a baked potato with lots of butter. Most soups, especially if they are homemade, are okay. If you have to feed some cooked chicken or fish, then that is what you have to do. I would not advise any other cooked meats because of the high grease content.

Be sure to keep on hand enzymes and probiotics (beneficial enzymes and friendly bacteria) for you and your animals. You will need enzymes and intestinal flora more than ever when you are both eating foods that your systems are not necessarily used to. A stabilized oxygen in a powder form is another suggestion, especially for dogs and cats that have constipation and hairball problems. (See Resources.)

For general drinking water and the water you are going to mix with your animals' food, it is best to buy distilled water and add liquid minerals. (See Resources.)

Water with electrolytes is now available. It is sometimes referred to as energy water or sports water, which contains minerals, such as potassium, calcium, magnesium, manganese and chromium that are excellent to refurbish the system. This sports water is particularly high in the minerals that are so important to a stressed system.

Another way to keep your animal well hydrated is to make up a raw meat broth. Two tablespoons of raw ground meat for every one cup of the sports water or distilled water suggested above. Just take a fork and mash the ground meat in the water. Your animal will love you for the extra flavor of the meat. They may drink as much of the raw meat broth as they desire. They can live on just water and meat for several days if they have to.

It's always a good idea to have homeopathic remedies and flower remedies handy. Some suggestions: Aconitum, apis mellifica, arsenicum album, bryonia, carbo vegetabilis, chamomilla, cocculus, ferrum phosphoricum, hepar sulphuricum, hypericum, lachesis, ledum, magnesia phosphorica, natrum muriaticum, nux vomica, phosphorus, pulsatilla, rhus toxicodendron, rutagraveolens, symphytum, urtica urens, Animal Emergency Care and Rescue Remedy.

Homeopathic travel kits and books are available and convenient to carry. If you are traveling by air, going through x-ray machines, get a lead film bag for your homeopathic remedies. I have a lead bag that is 6 inches by 12 inches and my homeopathic travel kit fits in it perfectly.

CHAPTER 13

DETOXIFICATION

Detoxify means to rid of poisons or the effects of poison. Poison is defined as any substance that has an inherent tendency to destroy life or impair health.

Pesticides, chemicals, devitalized food and vaccinations all set up toxic situations in the system. The body must rid itself of these poisons.

We see symptoms of detoxification with vomiting, diarrhea, bad breath, itchy skin, draining eyes and ears, and cysts and tumors, to name a few.

After your animals start eating fresh foods, their bodies will detoxify because they now have the nutrients to build healthy systems and no longer will have the need to suppress disease. You will notice it more with some animals than with others.

Detoxification can start immediately or it may take days, weeks or months before the animal's body is healthy enough to detoxify.

Usually the body will detoxify through areas that are already diseased. For instance, dogs who have skin problems will detoxify through the skin. The itching and body odors sometimes get worse at first because the system initially heals internally and releases the toxins or poisons through the skin.

I wish I could tell you how long it will take, but each system is so different I can only say I have seen animals get better in a couple of weeks, and I have seen skin disorders that continued for months.

At least animals on the fresh food program continue on an upward spiral, getting healthier and healthier as each day progresses.

Animals on antibiotics, antihistamines, hormones or cortisone appear not to have problems for awhile, because drugs suppress disease, but it always comes back and even worse than before once you discontinue the drugs. It goes without saying that the side effects of drugs can be more deadly than the disease.

Whatever your animal encounters in the way of detoxification, there is a natural way to take care of it: FHES, Colostrum, Aloe Vera Concentrate, C+Plus, PuriZone+Plus and many other natural foods.

A simple solution for the dog with skin problems is constant bathing. Have you ever been hot and sweaty and felt itchy all over? That's a form of detoxification. The bacteria builds up on the skin and causes the itchiness. Taking a bath or shower will relieve the discomfort by getting rid of the poisons that are sitting on the skin.

The same is true for your animal. Whenever the body is detoxifying through the skin, that skin needs to be kept free of poisons that are coming out of the system and causing the itching. Some animals may need to be bathed every day for a few days. Even though it takes a great deal of time, effort and care during that healing process, keep in mind how intense that itching sensation is.

If you were suffering from a severe case of poison ivy, poison oak or chicken pox, that would give you an idea how intense the itchiness is for your animal. Keep that in mind when you see your dog or cat scratching incessantly.

Dogs and cats do not scratch just because they are bored or because it's a nervous habit. They scratch because they itch. Take away the cause of the itch and they will quit scratching.

When you first see your dog or cat scratching, do something about it right away. The more serious it becomes, the longer it takes to heal.

Natural remedies that can be used for healing are Aloe Vera Concentrate, A+Plus, AnimaLife, Calcium+Plus, C+Plus, Colloidal Silver, Colostrum, FHES (Flanagan Hydrogen Enhanced Silica), MSM (Organic Sulfur), ProEnergy, PuriZone+Plus, ReVive and ReStore. (See Resources.)

FleaBane (Erigeron) 3-in-1, Colloidal Silver and Colostrum Cream can be used externally for red, irritated skin. These products will absorb into the skin and give soothing relief to raw areas.

For the eyes and nose, Colloidal Silver is an excellent antibacterial, antiviral and antifungal agent. Use a glass dropper and put several drops at a time directly into the nostrils or eyes.

For the ears, first clean with a gauze pad wrapped around your finger; then put enough Colloidal Silver in the ears to fill the canal; gently massage them for a few minutes to give the Colloidal Silver a chance to down into the canal and loosen the debris. When you stop massaging, your animal will shake his/her head and whatever has accumulated in the ears will come flying out.

Topical use of Colloidal Silver for hot spots, rashes, mange, parasites, open wounds or sores: spray or apply with dropper directly onto the infected area.

To purify water with Colloidal Silver: Add one ounce to each gallon of distilled water. Shake well; wait ten minutes; shake again; wait another ten minutes and it is ready to drink.

Colloidal Silver

A colloid is a liquid containing microscopic particles of substances that do not actually dissolve in the solution, but are so minute as to remain suspended in the liquid. Colloidal Silver is a suspension of highly charged ultra-microscopic clusters of pure silver in distilled water.

Colloidal Silver is shown to be effective against more than 650 disease-causing organisms, including E coli, and it is an antifungal agent hostile to Candida, Candida globate and M. furfur.

Microorganisms depend on a specific enzyme to breathe, Colloidal Silver is a catalyst that disables these enzymes. Colloidal Silver is an immune system ally that serves as a first line sheath of protection against the various pathogens attacking the body.

Hypericum made from the herb, St. Johnswort, is especially helpful when there is intense itching, particularly the legs and paws. For dogs who are constantly chewing at their feet or who have caused lick granulomas (a spot on the body, usually the legs or feet, where constant licking has caused a calloused area, tumor or growth) use hypericum ointment, rather than a liquid form, because it is easier to apply. Hypericum ointment can be applied several times a day for relief.

All the homeopathic remedies if they are licked off will do as much good internally for your animal as externally. That's one of the wonderful perks of using natural products.

In fact, only products that are edible should be put on your dog or cat because everything that's put on the outside goes inside while they're grooming themselves.

Sometimes detoxification comes in the form of loose stools for a few days or even weeks. The stools have the consistency of mashed potatoes. That is a cleansing.

If your animal has diarrhea, which is the consistency of water, this is a whole different matter and you have something going on besides detoxification. Do not confuse the two.

Diarrhea needs immediate professional attention because it causes dehydration which can be fatal.

Often the stools will be encased in mucous. A healthy system gets rid of the mucous because it is no longer needed. Worms will also come out in the stools now because the worms cannot live without the mucous. The whole process of detoxifying is a magnificent manifestation of healing.

Your animal's urine may have a strong odor for a few days. Again, this is a cleansing. As your animal gets healthier you will notice more urine and your animal will urinate for a longer period of time at each urination, which is a very healthy sign.

You may notice that the eyes are draining. Everything from a thin watery discharge to thick mucous in varying colors will drain from one or both eyes. All is well. Let the toxins come out. The animal is getting rid of poisons out of any and all orifices that he or she can.

When guardians tell me about the first signs of improvement they often say, "My animal's eyes are so bright and clear now. "Other comments are: "He's more like himself now." "She's just like a puppy again." "He's as playful as a kitten." The sweet temperament and the playful personality begin to emerge. Now, that's healing!

In order to reach that point your animal must go through the detoxification. For some animals you may not notice any aggravations. For others, it may be a constant uphill road. There is no way of predicting.

What you do know for sure is that each day your dogs and cats eat good fresh food they are going in the right direction, towards good health.

Free Radicals And Poor Health

Free radicals are electrically charged molecules that attack unprotected cells. These attacks wreak havoc on key cellular activities causing the cells to lose their DNA structure and function. Cells thus damaged become stagnate and sites of cancer and growths. Exposure to toxins, viruses, germs, fungi or environmental pollutants can increase a generation of free radicals in the body which lead to the acceleration of the aging process, arthritis and other inflammatory diseases, kidney disease, cataracts, inflammatory bowel syndrome, colitis, lung dysfunction, pancreatitis, skin lesions, cancer and/or a severely taxed immune system. For combating the ill effects of free radicals exercise and a good antioxidant is important.

CHAPTER 14

HOW MUCH DO I FEED?

Every kitten/cat and every puppy/dog needs a different amount of food each time they eat, just as people do. It is how the body metabolizes the food that decides how much is necessary.

Companies who put on their labels the amount a certain size dog or cat should eat each day is ludicrous. How much are you going to eat at your next meal? People aren't even sure what they themselves are going to eat during any given day, so how can they possibly guess what their animal is going to eat?

Do you feed your children based on how many pounds they weigh? Do you prepare so many cups per pound of body weight? Of course, not. You put so much food on the table that you know your family will eat until they are full and usually you have leftovers. That's how it should be for your animals.

Adult cats and dogs should be offered food once a day. Each time you put the food down, put so much on the plate or in the bowl that they cannot possibly finish it.

If they have been eating dry or canned foods, they may eat a huge amount of raw food at first to reach their nutrition satiation level or they may go to the other extreme and not eat at all, because the food smells foreign to them. Whatever the situation, analyze it and make your best judgment as to how to get them started on the raw food. Some animals eat it immediately and all is well. Others have a difficult time even deciding to eat it, and a few actually go through some tough detoxification.

NEVER starve your animal out. It absolutely does not work for cats! They will starve until they are dehydrated and very ill. For a young, relatively healthy, cat or dog, they

---

How Often Do I Feed And When?

Look forward to reduced dental problems, skin problems, flea problems, ear problems, bowel problems and more. It is possible, IF you raise your dog or cat with a variety of raw food and supplements with plenty of exercise and away from chemicals and drugs. You must also feed your healthy adult dog or cat no more than once a day; sick animals, puppies and kittens need to be fed more often. Feeding no more than once a day is essential because their bodies are designed to work hard and quick so raw meat does not putrefy in the digestive tract. To feed a healthy dog or cat more than once a day forces the system to overwork. Their bodies are meant to gorge, so they must be given as much as they will eat at each feeding. A simple treat would suffice when your animal seems hungry; rib bones, marrow bones, chicken backs, necks, knuckle bones, hearts, etc, all raw, of course.

---

can go a day or two without eating; however, when in doubt always see that they eat once within 48 hours.

You can mix the raw food with food they are already used to; you can give a favorite people food to bribe them; you can hand feed them; pretend it's a treat, using the tone of voice you usually use when giving a treat. Whatever you have to do to keep them eating, do it. Try not to go back to giving just cooked food, always mix in a little of the raw. It's called tough love. I know you and your animal will soon work things out.

Never feed dry food dry. Soak dry food in water before feeding or mixing with raw food. Dry food is the worst garbage that has ever been perpetrated on our animals. It destroys the kidneys, pancreas, liver; causes gastric torsion (bloat), to name a few of the serious ailments it causes.

Puppies and kittens should be fed on demand. They will usually wean themselves onto the raw food on their own by starting to eat out of mom's plate whenever they feel like it. Here again, some kittens/puppies may have a few nibbles at two weeks; some will eat full meals at three weeks; others may not start for another week or two. Whenever they are ready, they and their mothers will know when it is time.

After they are completely weaned, they will let you know how many times a day they want to eat. Healthy kittens/puppies are usually very vocal when they are hungry. Puppies/kittens up to the age of 4 months should be fed on demand. They get to eat all they want to eat as often as they want to eat. Remember, in the first year of a kitten/puppy's life, they grow as much as a person grows in 15 years.

This program of allowing them to eat as much as they want at each meal can only be used if you are feeding healthy raw food; canned and dry food won't work, because they never reach the point of being nutritionally satisfied. I repeat: nutritionally satisfied. Being stuffed full of junk food does not provide nutrients; it's just empty calories. The body is not interested in quantity; it is interested in quality.

Fat cats and dogs are starving. (This is true of people as well.) In other words, because their bodies cannot reach their nutrition satiation point, they continue to eat, hoping that they will finally be sated, but they can't be satisfied on junk food so the struggle goes on, and they get fatter and fatter, until they get the raw food they need.

CHAPTER 15

FLEAS, OUR FRIENDS

Healthy animals repel fleas. Flea problems are caused by nutritional deficiencies. One of the first symptoms of any ailing immune system is a dog or cat that is covered with fleas.

If you look at fleas in a positive way it is wonderful of them to let us know our animals are having problems.

Fleas are kept under control the same way other diseases and disorders are—by the immune system. For instance, parvovirus is an airborne virus. It is all around your dog at any given time. What keeps him from getting parvo? His immune system.

The same is true of fleas. If the animal's immune system is strong enough, the fleas will be repelled.

Fleas are parasites that are just here to do their job. That job is to suck blood from dead, diseased, dying and disabled animals. Then another insect or animal comes along to do their job and on it goes so that we can live in a clean environment without carcasses stacked to the heavens.

The fleas don't know that the animal they are eating is your companion animal. They just know this dog or cat is not well and fits their criteria for lunch.

Your animals may all eat the same food, sleep in the same place, be given the same love and attention and yet one animal has arthritis, another has ear mites, another licks and chews at his hot spots all day and another has fleas. Each animal's body manifests its individual problems in its own unique way.

We are told that fleas cause skin and coat problems. Actually it is the other way around. First the animal has the skin problem (or some other disorder) and that attracts the fleas.

Skin and coat problems are major complaints of our companion animals. The symptoms appear mostly during the summer months because the body uses more fatty acids during hot weather. It is not because the dog or cat has the problem only during the summer, but because it becomes evident externally during that time. You see excessive scratching, chewing, licking, dry, flaky skin, matted coats, loss of hair, eczema, hot spots, and what is referred to by many as "flea bite dermatitis or flea allergy." These problems are caused by an immune system that is malnourished.

The raw food program will build up the immune system to repel the fleas, heal the skin and coat and strengthen the body.

A completely balanced diet is the key. No one vitamin, mineral or herb is the answer. People excitedly tell me they have finally found the secret to controlling fleas—a vitamin, mineral or compound that is THE answer to end all fleas. Sooner or later it becomes evident that it wasn't the "panacea" it was cracked up to be.

Even though some elements work for a short time, after awhile the body becomes unbalanced again.

For instance, adding a few vitamins or minerals to processed food may help for a short time, but when the body continues to be deficient in other nutrients, over a period of time it again becomes out of balance, often worse than before.

The body must be given a balanced diet. The animal's system can then decide which nutrients it needs at any given time.

Pesticides

The answer to flea problems is not pesticides. Poisons only make the situation worse. Just the cautions on the labels should frighten you enough to discourage your use of these deadly poisons. "Harmful if swallowed." "Harmful if absorbed through the skin." "Avoid breathing spray mist." "Avoid contact with human skin." "Wear rubber gloves when applying flea dip."

Products that are dangerous for humans are also dangerous for animals. They have the same delicate organs we do. Their skin absorbs poisons just like ours. They have respiratory systems that breathe. They have livers that must detoxify all poisons coming into the system.

When the skin, lungs and liver cannot keep up with the detoxification, animals become seriously ill, sometimes resulting in death. Pesticides are poisons. They are deadly to our companion animals and to us.

People resort to pesticides because they are told the answer is to kill the fleas. It is not possible to kill all the fleas in and around your house and yard any more than it is possible to kill all bacteria. Fleas are extremely resilient.

We will never see the end of them in our lifetime. Nor do we want to. All bacteria and parasites serve a very important purpose on this planet.

What we really want is for our companion animals to be free of all parasites. Put your time and effort into keeping your animals healthy and you will not have to spin your wheels fighting fleas.

Many of you already know that even when you use pesticides you don't get the results you want. The fleas may be gone for a few hours or days, but ultimately they come back in force and, worst of all, the whole family, people and animals, have now been exposed to these deadly poisons, not to mention the expense.

The frustration of seeing an animal suffer from flea bites and the irritation to the skin from the saliva of the flea is enough to make anyone reach out for an immediate solution. That is understandable.

The problem lies in the fact that the situation is eventually made worse by using pesticides, thereby lowering the animal's resistance to the fleas even more.

Because we cannot actually see the liver in our animals desperately fighting the toxins that are being absorbed through the skin from a flea dip, and we cannot feel the pain in the lungs with every breath inhaled from the fumes of a flea collar, spray or powder, most people do not realize the severity of the damage that is done.

The numerous, complicated functions of the liver, lungs and skin are indispensable. Only through their ability to expel poison are they able to keep the toxicity of drugs, pesticides and other chemicals from killing our animals.

Nature did not create insecticides or pesticides, so neither the body nor the environment can assimilate or break down these man-made chemicals.

We would not have the existing epidemic of fleas if we had healthy animals and a wholesome environment. Because we are not taking care of our planet, we are seeing the worst infestation of parasites ever, and it continues to grow worse each year. We are working against Mother Nature rather than with her. Let's turn that around.

Plants and animals lived on this planet for millions of years without destroying it. We could do the same.

Anemia

Anemia is another serious consequence of flea infestation. Anemia is the lack of sufficient red blood cells and oxygen in the blood. Between a poor diet and fleas literally sucking the blood out of an animal your dog or cat can be suffering from poor blood.

The symptoms are general weakness, lethargy, paleness (check the gums inside the mouth), abdominal pain, and subsequently, loss of appetite. Fleas are not just bothersome, they are a real health problem.

Tapeworms

Tapeworms, which are carried into the system of the dog or cat by fleas, can also cause anemia. Here again, if your animal is healthy, the tapeworm cannot establish itself for the worm must have mucous deposits in which to set up housekeeping.

Worms can be eliminated with natural substances such as herbs, fig powder or homeopathic remedies.

You Are The Consumer

As long as you are buying canned and dry foods, brewers yeast, flea collars, sprays, powders, dips and shampoos, the manu-facturers will continue to provide them. It is up to you to change the trend. Don't assume that because these items are bad for your animal's health that our government or the manufacturers are going to make any changes. You have to make them make the changes. Commercial animal products are a multi-billion dollar business. If you stop buying them, the manufacturers will very quickly start figuring out what you will buy.

The time and energy spent on providing a balanced diet will pay for itself a hundredfold —no more junk food, no more pesticides, no more veterinary bills.

Take Action

Nothing speaks louder than where you spend your money. Thankfully, the popularity of the Internet has lots of consumer groups advocating your right to chemically free food and natural products. Our bodies were not designed to handle the onslaught of toxins under our kitchen cabinets, in our drinking water, air and food supply. There are many alternative brands with natural products that really work and are comparable in price to what you are used to paying especially when you take into consideration the amount of tax dollars it costs to clean our drinking water once you've used a chemical based detergent, as opposed to an enzyme-based one.

If you have access to the Internet, search for these consumer groups, visit their web sites and get involved. Simple email forms are set up to forward directly to your member of Congress. It can be very simple with the Internet's technology. Get involved and take action.

NATURAL FLEA CONTROL

While you are building up the immune system with the fresh food program, here are several methods of topical flea control that you can use safely and effectively.

Using a flea comb regularly on your dogs and cats will help you to see if in fact there are any fleas. If so, a flea comb is a very safe way to remove them.

Keep a cup of water with a few drops of dish detergent handy to contain the live fleas, otherwise they will get away from you. Fleas have respiratory systems and they will drown.

Erigeron (Canadian Fleabane) (See Resources) is an herb that repels fleas effectively with a pleasant aroma. Pennyroyal, eucalyptus and citronella may all work to some extent to repel fleas, but their strong odor is often overwhelming.

Erigeron has a soft, clean aroma that is not bothersome to animals. The oil of erigeron should be wiped or sprayed on the animal once a day for a few days until there is a buildup of the herb on the animal's skin and coat. Then it can be repeated every few days or once a week as needed.

The oil-based erigeron will also soothe the

skin and help to heal the hot spots that are caused by the saliva of the flea.

Erigeron is as effective internally as externally. Internally it aids digestion. When your animal licks and grooms him/herself the digestive system will benefit as well.

Also there is a new colloidal product (See Resources) which is extremely safe, non-toxic, non-caustic, biodegradable and a super active wetting agent that will penetrate and emulsify the skeletal form of the flea. The micelles break up the shell of the flea and cause it to dissolve.

The reason this will not harm your dog or cat is because they have a different skeletal structure. When using this erigeron colloidal product you will notice that it softens and soothes the skin.

Do not use brewers yeast, diatomaceous earth, salt or anything else topically on your animal that should not be ingested. Everything you put on the outside of your animals eventually goes to the inside when they groom themselves.

The Defleaing Touch
Tender touching benefits us all.

This feeling is so important to all beings. That's why animals touch, rub and groom each other.

Animal massage eliminates fleas by improving circulation and promoting healing. Remember, whenever your animals have fleas, they are telling you they are not well.

Touch, massage and acupressure are essential modalities in holistic health care. Learn more about them for both people and animals through books and seminars.

Bathing

Frequent bathing is important for animals with flea problems. Use only gentle shampoos. Do not use strong, poisonous shampoos, such as flea and tick, tar or sulfur or pyrethrins. All of these are irritating to the skin and toxic to the animal's entire system. They can be fatal. Do not use baby shampoos or dish detergents. They are said to be mild and gentle. Not so. They cut oil and grease, including your animal's natural oils.

Mild herbal shampoos soothe the body while cleansing. Chemically free shampoos for dry, flaky skin mild enough for those animals with hot spots and rashes are most beneficial.

Now available are shampoos that are sodium laurel sulfate free (See Resources) that treat our animals as gently as if they were washed with Mother Nature's gentlest rain.

The most important part of the bath is the rinsing. Rinse and rinse and rinse; then rinse again. Leaving any shampoo residue will irritate and dry the skin.

After and in-between shampoos use any of the natural tonics to control the fleas and soothe and heal the skin.

Vacuuming

Vacuum your carpeting often. That's where the fleas hang out.

About once a month sprinkle salt, regular table salt, on your carpet. The salt will sift down into the carpeting within a couple of days. After it does you can vacuum again as often as necessary.

When you first apply the salt to your carpet you may notice more fleas than ever. That's because they are being stirred up and are trying to escape.

Fleas groom themselves just like cats. When they take in a grain or two of salt while grooming, they become dehydrated which causes them to be disoriented and then they cannot reproduce. After taking in enough salt the adults will eventually die. Because of their life cycle you may continue to see fleas for a period of time until the eggs and larvae mature.

Do not put salt on scatter rugs, tile, hardwood floors or any surface where the salt cannot sift through, because it will stick to the feet of your animals and they will ingest it while grooming themselves.

Do not confine your animals to the house just to avoid fleas. They need to be out in the sunlight and fresh air. If their immune systems are not functioning properly they are going to get fleas no matter where they are.

CHAPTER 16

HOMEOPATHY & CHIROPRACTIC

Approximately 90 percent of all the animals I work with get well just from the fresh food program. The other 10 percent have stubborn or deep-seated problems that require other modalities like homeopathy and chiropractic therapy.

Homeopathy is a science based on the Law of Similars, let likes be cured by likes.

In other words, if a particular substance is taken by a healthy individual in large doses, it will produce specific symptoms of illness. However, when this same substance is taken in infinitesimal doses, it will stimulate the body's system to relieve these same symptoms.

An example is Ipecac. If taken in large quantities, it causes vomiting. If taken in small doses, it cures vomiting.

The substance from which the homeopathic remedy is made does not have a direct action of its own. It is the energy of the substance. That's why a mineral like arsenicum album (arsenic) can be given therapeutically.

When taken in a homeopathic dose—so infinitesimal it cannot be detected by traditional chemical tests—arsenicum album does not act as a poison, but produces a healing reaction within the diseased body.

Homeopathic remedies are prepared from animal, plant and mineral substances—from bees to marigolds to sulphur—with new remedies being added worldwide everyday. They number in the thousands.

Homeopathy works with the body's own intelligence—vital force—to keep the system in balance. Just as food attends to the body's nutritional balance, homeopathy cares for the vital force.

Both homeopathy and chiropractic are holistic, taking into account whenever one part of the body is out of balance, it affects the entire system.

If your animal appears to be "not her/himself," the natural health practitioner will ask questions that relate to the symptoms that you observe, not necessarily what disease, as an allopathic veterinarian would. And so the conversation goes until the homeopath or chiropractor has elicited enough information to establish a pattern. You must be part of this process, because no one knows your animal's habits or idiosyncrasies better than you. Beware of the practitioner who hustles your animal off into an examining room and without ten words with you starts injecting needles and giving pills. It is crucial to know as much about the animal's background as possible. And you need to stay with your animal during the entire examination.

One of the greatest advantages of homeopathy is that you become involved. In fact, you will learn to treat your own animals because of the necessity of your involvement while giving your animals' histories and by keeping a journal on their treatments.

We cannot rely on health practitioners alone. That's how we got ourselves into the mess we're in with western medicine. People go to MD's and DVM's and say, "I have such-and-such a problem, give me a pill." It's as much the client's fault as the practitioner. You often get what you ask for. If you want drugs, then you need to go to an allopathic veterinarian. If you want natural health care, then you need to know what you want and what to ask for, because there are very few truly holistic veterinarians.

Homeopathic remedies are given orally. The milk-sugar base from which they are made is pleasant to the palate. They come in the form of tiny tablets or pellets that dissolve quickly right in the mouth and do not have to be forced down your animal's throat.

Remedies are available in all sizes and potencies either in single bottles or multi-remedy kits. Ask your homeopathic pharmacist for help. While you are in the learning stage of homeopathy, I would stay within the 6X to 30X range in potencies and continue to consult with your present veterinarian.

Homeopathic remedies require special care. They should be kept in a clean, dry, dark, cool area, free from strong odors, such as camphor, perfumes, household cleaning materials, kitchen spices or herbs.

Do not refrigerate pellets and tablets, because they will absorb odors and moisture.

When giving a remedy to your animal, place the tablets in the cap of the bottle that the homeopathic remedy came in or in a clean, dry spoon. Empty the cap or spoon directly into your animal's mouth. Close his or her mouth and gently stroke the throat for 30 seconds while the tablets dissolve in the mouth. Be exceptionally gentle while holding your cat's mouth. Cats cannot swallow when their mouths are tightly closed.

Do not touch the tablets because they are made of a porous substance and will easily absorb germs from your hands. If you accidentally spill some tablets in your hand or on the floor, throw them away.

A bottle of 250 tablets costs only $4 to $5 and you may need as few as ten to twenty tablets to see your animal through an entire illness. If you take proper care of your remedies, they will last for years and years. No medical treatment of any kind is as inexpensive as homeopathy.

Don't let your present practitioner give your animal an antibiotic or steroid and send you on home. That's not getting down to the nitty-gritty. You don't want to suppress the problem. You want to get to the cause.

The best guarantee against getting yourself and your animal into an emergency situation is to become more aware of subtle symptoms of ill health. Don't wait until your animal is in a crisis before you become knowledgeable about natural health care. Encourage your veterinarian to read books and to attend courses on homeopathy. Do the same for yourself. Many books and seminars are available.

Prompt homeopathic & chiropractic treatment can save your animal's life, avert pain and suffering and get to the cause of any problem.

Chiropractic care for animals, just as for people, works with the nerves and vertebrae. The spinal column is intended to protect the delicate spinal cord and the nerves leading from it. When there is a subluxation, or misalignment, it pinches the nerve, which causes interference and normal nerve function is cut off, causing not only functional problems and pain, but ailments affecting every other part of the body.

Very few veterinarians practice chiropractic care, so you may have to consult your own chiropractor to see if they will check your animals and will give adjustments.

Homeopathic Remedies

The following list of remedies outlines various conditions, diseases and emergencies that can be treated with homeopathy. I have listed some of the most important ones.

Aconitum napellus: Fear, apprehension, stress, shock, sneezing, sore throat, cough.

Arnica montana: Trauma, shock, blows, falls, bruising, wounds, pain, teeth extraction, fractures, surgery, hemorrhage.

Arsenicum album: Vomiting, diarrhea, restlessness, respiratory ailments. Animal wants to be where it is warm.

Belladonna: Heat stroke, fever, pain, redness, swelling, great thirst.

Carbo vegetabilis: Collapse, flatulency, animal is cold and clammy, drop in body temperature (normal is 101.5 degrees).

Cocculus indicus: Motion sickness, vomiting, drooling, inability to open mouth or swallow, epilepsy.

Hypericum perfoliatum: Any type of nerve injury, especially to feet, toes and tail, spinal injuries, after any surgery.

Ledum palustre: Puncture wounds, animal or insect bites, eye injuries.

Nux vomica: Vomiting, diarrhea or constipation with straining, irritability, indigestion, bloated after eating.

Phosphorus: Frightened by thunder storms, fireworks or any sudden loud noise. Vomiting right after eating, blood in urine. Animal wants to be where it is cold.

Rhus toxicodendron: Stiff, slow to get up after sleeping, skin problems with excessive scratching.

Silicea: Abscesses from thorns or splinters, swollen glands, epilepsy.

Sulphur: Skin problems, fleas, mange, strong body odor, diarrhea, vomiting.

Thuja occidentalis: Warts, ill-effects from vaccination including skin disorders, lethargy, loss of appetite.

Urtica urens: Burns, urinary blockage.

This information is meant as an introduction into the wonderful world of Mother Nature's elements that are being used to heal—naturally.

EPILOG

I wish we had an animal nutrition center on every corner and a holistic veterinary practitioner right down the block. But we don't.

Because of this, we are seeing our animals suffer from malnutrition in a world rich with wonderfully nutritious foods.

The best we can do for the moment is to care for our own animals, network with friends and become more knowledgeable on our own.

Encourage your present veterinarian to use natural healing. Talk to your groomers, trainers, kennel and cattery owners and let them know how they can get involved. It is hard for me to believe that anyone who loves and works with animals wouldn't want them to be healthy and happy. If feeding fresh food accomplishes this, why wouldn't people in the business of veterinary medicine and grooming, training and caretaking be interested?

Nutrition is not taught in veterinary schools at the present time, so we can't expect orthodox practitioners to even be aware of the possibilities of natural healing. Pet shop owners get their expertise in nutrition from commercial pet food companies and so far they have not shown an interest in providing fresh food.

This book is intended to open a path to old-time nutrition. We used to feed ourselves and our animals much better quality food many years ago when we were eating foods right from the farm. Progress has brought us processed foods, preservatives, pesticides, drugs and radiation, none of which are digestible.

Common sense tells us that we must take care of the beings on this planet the way Mother Nature intended with good food, safe shelter and affection for each other.

I don't believe there is a greater love than that which people have for their animals or that animals have for their guardians. Even other human beings do not understand us the way our animals do.

Can you imagine the difference in this world if every child had a snuggley animal and if every school, business, prison, hospital and convalescent home had loving companion animals?

Maybe your encouragement will bring about a much-needed change.

About the Author

Twenty-five years ago Pat McKay rescued a deformed, malnourished, five-week-old Doberman. Because of the severity of the puppy's condition she was told by several practitioners to destroy the dog.

Pat already had a two-year-old Doberman at home on a good diet and thought she would see what could be done. With a few additional nutrients added to the fresh food diet, the puppy was walking a mile a day within three months. Not only had she improved in general health, the pup no longer had any deformity in her legs.

Without realizing it at that time, a sound nutrition program was born.

During the past thirty years while Pat McKay was studying ways to help her own digestive problems she realized the importance of proper nutrition for each individual species. She has been and is now continuing to search for ways to improve natural health care for carnivores through healthy foods and organic supplements.

Her studies have included attending allopathic, homeopathic and holistic seminars and conferences all over the country for animals and people. The information is then extrapolated into nutrition and natural health programs for dogs and cats.

During the 1980s she owned and operated the Pat McKay Nutrition Center in the mid-Wilshire area of Los Angeles. In addition to nutrition consultations and classical homeopathy for dogs and cats, the business included grooming, boarding and retail/wholesale nutrition supplements for animals. In 1983 Pat formulated her own line of vitamin-mineral-herbal supplements.

In 1988 she decided to retire and moved to Eugene, Oregon. During the next two years she published a newsletter about animal nutrition which led to writing her first book, *REIGNING CATS & DOGS, Good Nutrition, Healthy, Happy Animals.*

She returned to Los Angeles in 1990 to continue writing and lecturing. In 1993 there was an overwhelming need to again provide a nutrition support program for clients and their animals. She then offered consultations, nutrition supplements and ready-to-eat meals. This business grew so quickly in two years that she now has a company called Pat McKay, Inc, in Pasadena, California.

Her most recent book *NATURAL IMMUNITY, Why You Should NOT Vaccinate!* is a handbook for health practitioners across the country.

Her present companions are Reigndrop, a five-year-old, ebony-spotted oriental tabby, two Borzois (Russian wolfhounds), Sergei and Toli, 2-1/2 years old, and Jacques, a standard poodle, 2 years old. Of course all Pat's animals are on her fresh, raw food program, including naturally grown meats and vegetables, organic, plant-cell-grown, vitamin/mineral supplements — and no vaccinations. An hour and a half run in the park every morning doesn't hurt either.

Resources

Pat McKay, Inc
Healthy Foods for Dogs and Cats
396 West Washington Boulevard
Pasadena, CA 91103
626.296.1120
626.296.1122 Nutrition/Information/Consultation
626.296.1126 FAX
1.800.975.7555 Order Line
email: patmckay@gte.net
website: www.patmckay.com

Pat McKay Organics

Aloe Concentrate	MSM
AnimaLife	PhytoFoods
A+Plus	ProEnergy
Bribery	PuriZone+Plus
Calcium+Plus	ReStore
C+Plus	ReVive
Colloidal Silver	Squiggles Ginger Cookies
Colostrum	Squiggles Carob Cookies
CoQ10	3% FoodGrade H2O2
Gelatin	FleaBane Shampoo
Isoflavones	Herbal Shampoo
Lecithin	Herbal Hair Conditioner
Lifestar Vitamin E	FleaBane Solution
Liver Lovers	FleaBane 3-in-1

Pat McKay Books

REIGNING CATS & DOGS
Good Nutrition, Healthy
Happy Animals

NATURAL IMMUNITY
Why You Should NOT
Vaccinate!

INDEX

Testimonials

"Balanced raw food diets make the most sense from a natural and scientific point of view."

—Michael Lemmon, DVM, Renton, WA

"I've been a big fan of the fresh food approach for a long time. With everyone's schedule so busy, busy, busy, it's wonderful to finally have REIGNING CATS & DOGS as a guide, which makes it so easy to do!"

—Carolyn Blakey, DVM, Richmond, IN

"The object in creating optimal health and nutrition is to study each animal's habitat and food sources; then custom make diets that most closely resemble their own natural (original) diet."

—Jeff Brisco, Senior Animal Nutritionist, LosAngeles Zoo

"An acknowledged pioneer and leader in the development of the raw and fresh foods diet is animal nutritionist-consultant-author, Pat McKay. Nationally recognized for her work by veterinarians and other animal health care professionals, McKay has devoted more than twenty years to researching and completing hundreds of case studies. Her findings consistently have revealed that a raw foods program ensures maximum health results for her animal clients."

—Rhona Zaid, PhD, Los Angeles, CA

"Preventive health care through optimal nutrition should be the goal."

—Francis Kallfelz, DVM, Professor of Clinical Nutrition
New York State School of Veterinary Medicine/Cornell

"We are seeing disease conditions in animals that we did not see years ago. Many of these may be traced to nutrition as the source, and this may have started in previous generations and are now manifesting themselves as clinical entities. McKay is helping to promote the concept that nutrition is vitally important in all health fields."

—Don Lundholm, DVM, Huntington Beach, CA

"Finally, here's the book that says what all holistically oriented veterinarians have known, that with fresh wholesome foods, physical and emotional health can be built and maintained on a daily basis, rather than suppressed and/or palliated with the crisis eliminative approach."

—Neal Weiner, DVM, Lewiston, CA

"Pat McKay has given us an important and timely book. This is a subject of great importance that demands attention from everyone. Clearly, it is time to begin an open and rational discussion of this topic."

—Ron Carsten, DVM, MS, Glenwood Springs, CO

Testimonials (cont.)

"My dog, Kaiser, as a young pup swallowed a piece of wire, puncturing his intestine. During the next year he had two surgeries, removal of his ileocecal valve and one-half of his intestine; he was extremely thin, had a dull coat, cracking foot pads, pale gums, continuous diarrhea and vomiting. He was dying a slow death. Then I found Pat McKay."

"Today at 3 years old, Kaiser's blood tests are now perfect. He has such a beautiful, shiny, silvergray Weimaraner coat that people stop us wherever we are to ask about him. There is no doubt in my mind that without Pat McKay, her diet, homeopathy, and her caring guidance, my baby Kaiser wouldn't be with me today. His progress has been incredible!"
—Debborah Lang, La Jolla, CA

"Our guardians have been feeding us the raw foods that Pat McKay advises for five years, and we are feeling great, are never sick and the food is deeelicious!"
—Ferdy, Misky & Squeaky, Alhambra, CA

"With chiropractic being my profession for over thirty years, I am keenly aware of the positive influence on the health and well-being of individuals who chose to eat, drink, breathe, rest, exercise and think in the healthiest manner available. Good nutrition is an area of increased interest and research in recent years, and we are just as interested in the health of our animals— presently three dogs and five cats."

"Thank goodness for Pat McKay arriving on the scene. Pat is a caring, informed and educated lady who has devoted most of her life learning and teaching others how to give animals a healthier lifestyle. We have followed the recommendations in her book for approximately three years. None of our animals know what sickness is. We highly recommend her work."
—Sally & Jerry Lakin, DC, Lake Havasu City, AZ

"I've found that Pat McKay's Raw Food Diet has been a key factor in improving the health and well-being of animal companions. A number of seriously ailing animals that I have treated might not have survived and recovered without the support of Pat's diet. Even more, regular use of the diet works for animals who are well and can bring them into robust and joyful health."

"Pat's clear and simple instructions make the diet easy to follow. I highly recommend the diet to anybody who has a beloved animal companion."
—Naomi L. Gulden, Feline Nutritionist, Lehigh Valley, PA

Testimonials (cont.)

"Our six-and-a-half-year-old pug, Eames, suffered from colitis since he was two years old. He vomited constantly; had chronic diarrhea, and sometimes had both simultaneously. Eames had very expensive diagnostic tests and scopes. We tried everything the vets recommended. He took daily steroids, two stomach and bowel medications, plus antibiotics. When his stomach and colon would not relax, we had to drug him with tranquilizers."

"On June 1, 1995, Eames began Pat McKay's raw food diet. HE NO LONGER TAKES ANY MEDICINE!!! He has NO stomach or bowel disorders. Even our vets have been very supportive. They are delighted that he is cured."
—Ron Winokur & Dennis Bogorad, West Los Angeles, CA

"Our re-education regarding the feeding of animals was jolted into high gear when our then eleven-year-old catfriend Apollo began to fail dramatically. Through some miracle we still can't figure out, we were led to Pat McKay. She advised us quite firmly that Apollo might not make it, but insisted that we treat him homeopathically and start the raw food diet."

"What we learned and observed turned our ignorant understanding of animal care completely upside down. There were times when we didn't know if Apollo would be alive in the morning, but he stayed with us, seemingly telling us, "This is all about you guys learning something—so get with it!"

"That was nearly four years ago, and the purring mound of warm orange fluff basking in a ray of morning sunshine today graces our lives with joy and amazement."

"There are simply no excuses to keep feeding our animal friends dead and empty food. We urge everyone we meet to read Pat's book. Her gutsy integrity is not something to take lightly or try to foolishly explain away. She is offering us all some very wise instruction about the humane and intelligent feeding of our loving companions."
—Mark Knowles & Don Keller, Sierra Madre, CA

"Pat McKay's caring, enlightened, innovative and current approach to optimum health maintenance for our domestic animal friends has no equal. My dogs and I have greatly benefited from—and been enriched by—our ten-year association with Pat, both personally and as an institution."
—Robert Suchoski, Altadena, CA

Testimonials (cont.)

"I thank Pat McKay for opening the door to changes in my animals' lives as well as my own. It was at her animal nutrition lecture that I first was exposed to homeopathy, a natural medicine, that is now a way of life for me."

"Now as a homeopath, I work with animals and see wonderful life-changing results due to the raw meat diet and use of homeopathy. Her book is required reading for all my clients."

—Julie Mann, M.Hom, Los Angeles, CA

"Since my cats have been on Pat McKay's program they have been thriving. All their little ailments have disappeared. The healing power of a diet aligned with nature became most evident to me when I found a mange, flea-infested kitten with ear mites and watched her blossom into a beautiful healthy cat without drugs or toxic dips. All she had was Pat McKay's diet and, of course, lots of love. After reading REIGNING CATS & DOGS, I must say that my own diet has improved also."

—Dagmar Stansova, Topanga, CA

Pat McKay saved my 95 percent (according to my vet) dead dog's life by her recommendations, her supplements, her food and her care. I know he would not be here today if it were not for her. His progress, even in one week, was remarkable. My other twelve dogs are also doing so very well with her program. So much, much better than with dog food in stores.

—Virginia Swanson, Eagle Rock, CA

Dudley, my white Persian, has suffered with eye problems for over four years; I believe he was born with them. It became chronic this last six months. I tried everything: $1,000 later; the best opthalmologist; the last antibiotic (which cost $80) that "for sure would work"—well, it didn't. He was worse than ever. When I went to pick him up, he cried and hissed because the pain was so bad. At the end of my own strength, in tears, I prayed, "God help me." Well, He did. He sent me to Pat McKay and Art Stratton. Within twenty-four hours it was half way improved. By the third week, I'm happy to say he's healed. Thank God.

—Sharon Schauer, Sherman Oaks, CA

"We hear so much about save the whales, save the rhinos, save the condors— also, we can't neglect saving the animals that are right under our very noses, our best friends, our dogs and cats. REIGNING CATS & DOGS shows us the way."

—Terry Lee Haefer, CEO Advanced Enzyme Technologies,
Sherman Oaks, CA